How Fit Are We?

ISSUES
(formerly Issues for the Nineties)

Volume 49

Editor

Craig Donnellan

Independence
Educational Publishers
Cambridge

First published by Independence
PO Box 295
Cambridge CB1 3XP
England

© Craig Donnellan 2000

British Library Cataloguing in Publication Data
How Fit Are We? – (Issues Series)
I. Donnellan, Craig II. Series
613.7

ISBN 1 86168 120 8

Printed in Great Britain
The Burlington Press
Cambridge

Typeset by
Claire Boyd

Cover
The illustration on the front cover is by
Pumpkin House.

CONTENTS

Chapter One: A Question of Fitness

Chapter Two: Getting in Shape

Introduction

How Fit Are We? is the forty-ninth volume in the **Issues** series. The aim of this series is to offer up-to-date information about important issues in our world.

How Fit Are We? looks at obesity and getting in shape.

The information comes from a wide variety of sources and includes:
Government reports and statistics
Newspaper reports and features
Magazine articles and surveys
Literature from lobby groups
and charitable organisations.

It is hoped that, as you read about the many aspects of the issues explored in this book, you will critically evaluate the information presented. It is important that you decide whether you are being presented with facts or opinions. Does the writer give a biased or an unbiased report? If an opinion is being expressed, do you agree with the writer?

How Fit Are We? offers a useful starting-point for those who need convenient access to information about the many issues involved. However, it is only a starting-point. At the back of the book is a list of organisations which you may want to contact for further information.

*****

Survival of the fattest

They don't walk to school, they don't play games and their favourite occupation is watching telly: the result is mass obesity, truly a growing problem. By Emma Haughton

It's that time of year again. Having consumed many units of alcohol and several million calories above what is strictly necessary to keep body and soul together, we're all picking up the tab for seasonal over-indulgence. Chances are you're dusting off last year's list of exacting new year resolutions, planning that crash diet and just off to renew gym member-ship.

Long may your good intentions last, but perhaps it's not just your own health you should be worried about. If your kids spent Christmas slumped on the sofa in front of the TV, gorging themselves on chocolate Santas and selection packs, new bikes lying unused in the shed, they may well be more in need of a radical change of lifestyle than you are.

Because, according to a recent Government survey, our children are a pretty unhealthy bunch. *The Health of Young People 1995-97*, as the survey is called, is something of a misnomer: of the 20,000 it studied, no less than a third of those aged 16-24 were found to be overweight or obese. Today's youngsters are too lazy and gluttonous for their own good, it concluded, and present one of the greatest challenges to public health.

The survey results, however, come as no surprise to nutritionists and exercise experts, who are becoming increasingly concerned about young people's eating and exercise habits. 'Obesity is a growing problem,' says Dr Barbara Livingstone, lecturer in human nutrition at the University of Ulster. 'Children's body composition is changing, and it does appear that children are getting larger, with more fat at the expense of muscle tissue. And there's no reason to suggest that that trend will reverse.'

And, for once, it's not just parents who are to blame; schools, too, are failing to encourage children to adopt a more healthy lifestyle. Last October, many came under attack from the Government for the increasing proportion of junk food in their school meals. Around 3 million children have a school meal every day, and for a large proportion this is their main meal. But too many are filling up on burgers, chips and cakes, says the Government, which has drawn up the first set of nutritional guidelines in 18 years, stressing the need to offer more variety and balance.

'School meals are a real mine-field,' says Livingstone. 'Schools are in the business of making ends meet and tend to supply food that the children want to eat. Many do make an effort to encourage better eating habits and are working under enormous constraints, but never-theless there is a lot more that they can do to encourage appropriate food choices.'

However, with many pupils now able to go out to the shops at lunch time, reforming school meals may have a limited effect. And, ironically, it seems that when it comes to weight gain what goes in may not be as crucial as the energy subsequently expended. Despite the nation's expanding waistline, we are actually eating no more calories than we did two decades ago; nutritionists agree that inactivity, rather than diet, is the key element in obesity.

Take walking to school. In the mid 1970s, 72 per cent of children aged five-10 walked to school; now just 59 per cent do. Teenagers are even lazier – another Government report found that, in the decade to 1996, 11-15-year-olds had reduced their number of walks by 29 per cent – double the fall for the population as a whole.

This finding is backed by research by Professor Neil Armstrong, who measured the activity of 1,000 children aged five-16 by monitoring their heart rate. Although

boys are generally more active than girls, he found, activity decreases through primary school for both sexes, falling dramatically when they go on to secondary level.

'A lot of activities that were normal for children 10-20 years ago have been removed,' he says. 'With so few children walking to school now, many do not even experience the equivalent of a 10-minute brisk walk in the week – an important part of children's lifestyles that has been lost.' Indeed, research carried out at the Dunn Clinical Nutrition Centre, in Cambridge, in 1997 estimated that a child walking up to two miles a day to and from school would have used up a about half a day's food intake over a week.

The same is also true for cycling, says Armstrong. Although more children own bicycles, fewer ride them, particularly girls; while one in three boys with bicycles can ride on the roads, only one in nine girls is allowed to do so.

However, while few schools would view how children arrive at school as being under their jurisdiction, what happens after they go through the gates is also under question. Physical education has dropped too far down the curriculum, says Armstrong.

'Physical education in schools has been squeezed more and more since the national curriculum, especially with the introduction of the literacy and numeracy hours. PE time is going down, there's a fall in the number of qualified PE teachers, and schools are selling off playing fields for development. There may be a recommended minimum of two hours PE a week, but that's only a recommendation – the amount of time children spend in physical education is totally up to the school.'

But the problem is not just the quantity, but quality, says Susan Ebb, the head of nutrition and health at the Dunn centre, which has a facility for researching childhood obesity. Schools are focusing too much on team games which are often not the best activities for later life, she feels.

'Schools have got to get children going, encouraging them to be more active as children, but also setting up

---

'Schools have got to get children going, encouraging them to be more active as children, but also setting up the habits for life'

---

the habits for life,' she says. 'Schools like competitive activities – they get kudos from them, for instance – but girls especially hate team games. Many prefer individual activities such as aerobics.

'After all, not many people play hockey, netball or rugby in their thirties, but they may swim or go to exercise classes – we need to see much more emphasis on activities that carry through into adulthood.'

Like many observers, Ebb believes that education for life should embrace health as well as employability if we are to avoid a future population plagued by chronic illness. 'The problem is that people tend to get fatter as they get older.

'While children's innate fitness tends to keep them healthy, if you come into adulthood already overweight, it is extremely worrying to think where you will be in 50 years' time. And it's so difficulty to treat overweight adults, because it involves changing eating and exercise habits which are by then deeply ingrained.

'Everyone – parents, schools, health professionals – has got to take

---

The fats of life

- Overweight children are more likely to become overweight adults.
- Encouraging physical activity is the best way to ensure life-long health.
- Children who overeat are more likely to develop cancer in later life.
- Obesity raises the risk of heart disease.
- Slight obesity increases the risk of diabetes.
- Fatness is linked to early menstruation, a risk for hormone influenced cancer.

---

on board that we must improve the quality of life of our children. We can't afford to ignore it any longer. We have got to put good nutrition and exercise back into their lives.'

Suddenly people are waking up to what is going on, says Ebb, and it's not a moment too soon.

What children say about PE

'I do like PE, the theory and practical, but I wish we did more and other stuff like martial arts. That would be really useful.'

Simon, 15

'I hate games. I try and get out of it as often as I can.'

Tasha, 14

'Football's the worst. It's outside and I get muddy. And it's always freezing too.'

Jonathan, 13

'We have to wear short skirts and a matching top for PE. It's horrible if it's cold and you think all the boys are looking at you. Why can't we do music and dance instead? That would be cool.'

Holly, 15

What can parents do to help?

- A US study found a strong inverse relationship between television and losing weight. Children whose viewing is restricted often find something more active to do.
- Encourage your children to walk or cycle to school. If you are concerned about levels of traffic and safety, lobby your council to provide safe routes.
- The key role model for children is Mum, says Professor Armstrong. Children with an active mother tend to be more active than average.
- Remember that physical activity is the best investment in young people's health for life.

What can schools do?

- Take a hard look at your PE programme. Is it fostering a positive attitude to being active, or putting kids off physical activity for life? Are you focusing on all the children and not just the most talented 3-4 per cent? Do you offer alternatives to team games, such as aerobics, aqua fit or more co-operative activities? Could you offer more activities at lunchtime?

- Something as elementary as the PE kit can put a lot of children, especially girls, off games. Short skirts, in particular, may make them feel self-conscious and can be pretty chilly too.

- The main aim for school PE is to help develop a good foundation of motor skills. Skills such as throwing, kicking, and catching enable children to enjoy success with activities and sports in later life.
- Finding other ways to deal with the school run will ease traffic congestion and everyone's con-

science. Encourage parents to leave the car at home or, failing that, to organise more lift shares.
- School meals are important because of the kind of habits they foster and the messages children receive about a healthy diet.

• First published in *The Independent*, January, 1999. *©Emma Haughton*

English are among fattest in Europe

The epidemic of obesity sweeping Europe is threatening a public health catastrophe with dramatic increases in diabetes, heart and other diseases, international experts warned yesterday.

England comes near the top of the European league of fattest nations with 17 per cent of men and 20 per cent of women officially classified as obese. Only Germany and Finland have more fat men and only Russia and the Czech Republic have more fat women.

In a declaration signed by medical experts from 26 countries, the European Association for the Study of Obesity called on governments to tackle what it dubbed the 'silent epidemic'.

It says rates of obesity are rising in most countries and in some areas 40-50 per cent of the population are affected. No country has escaped but few have a national strategy for dealing with it.

The greatest concern is over the proportion of children who are overweight. Experts meeting at the European Congress of Obesity in Milan said in their Milan Declaration: 'Their future health and well-being is being put at risk through inaction on this issue.'

In England, obesity rates have risen two and a half times for women and almost tripled for men in two decades.

Since 1980, they have risen from eight to 20 per cent of women and from six to 17 per cent of men. Other countries have experienced similar

By Jeremy Laurance, Health Editor

rises as a result of increasingly sedentary lifestyles and a richer diet linked with growing prosperity.

Professor Jaap Seidell, president of the European Association for the Study of Obesity, said: 'There are signs that a larger proportion of the next generation are becoming obese

In England, obesity rates have risen two-and-a-half times for women and almost tripled for men in two decades

and overweight at an earlier age. While a great deal has been achieved in reducing levels of heart disease those gains could be wiped out by this threat.'

Professor Philip James, chairman of the International Obesity Task Force and architect of the Food Standards Agency in the UK, said: 'We need governments to sit up and listen. In some countries they are listening – many other countries have yet to take up the challenge. This is a global crisis and urgent action is required now to prevent this silent epidemic of serious illness and spiralling health costs. We are facing a health disaster if we do not act.'

Overall, almost one-third of people living in the European Union are overweight and one in 10 is obese.

*© The Independent
June, 1999*

Fat is a European issue

Prevalence of obesity (BMI>30) in a selection of European countries

Women	%	Men	%
1. Russia	27.9	1. Finland	19.0
2. Czech Republic	20.2	2. Germany	17.2
3. **England**	**20.0**	3. **England**	**17.0**
4. Germany	19.3	4. Czech Republic	16.3
5. Finland	19.0	5. **Scotland**	**15.9**
6. Belgium	18.4	6. Belgium	12.1
7. **Scotland**	**17.3**	7. Spain	11.5
8. Spain	15.2	8. Russia	10.8
9. Sweden	11.9	9. Denmark	10.0
10. France	10.5	10. Sweden	10.0
11. Netherlands	9.3	11. France	9.6
12. Denmark	9.0	12. Netherlands	8.4
13. Italy	6.3	13. Italy	6.5

Source: International Obesity Task Force

Physical activity, body-weight and health

How do we get people to be more physically active? Along with an excess in energy intake, physical inactivity is an important contributor to the ever-increasing levels of overweight and obesity. Dr John Kearney, Scientific Director of the Institute of European Food Studies, reports on a recent European study:[1]

From a public health perspective, the potential benefit from increasing population levels of physical activity (especially among those who are currently sedentary) is enormous in terms of stemming the growing rise in the obesity epidemic.

As with other lifestyle factors – smoking and diet – bringing about a sustained change involves a knowledge of people's attitudes and perceptions. In a recent pan-EU survey of 15,339 consumers (approximately 1,000 adults from each member state), the Institute of European Food Studies (IEFS) assessed their attitudes towards physical activity, body-weight and health as well as activity levels, and body weights and heights (all self-reported).

Weight loss is best achieved by combining changes in eating habits with increased amounts of physical activity. Physical activity is thought to be more effective in the prevention of overweight and obesity than in its treatment. Yet, results from this survey suggest that consumers perceive food to be far more important in preventing weight gain than physical activity. Similarly, when asked about the most important influences on health, nutrition ranked much higher than physical activity.

Consumers also perceived smoking and stress as more important health influences than physical activity. Furthermore, a quarter of the EU sample believed that unless physical activity resulted in weight loss, they were not really benefiting from it. These results suggest a need to increase consumers' awareness of the health benefits of a physically active lifestyle and weight maintenance.

This latest study on 'Consumer Attitudes towards Physical Activity' contrasts somewhat with results from an earlier survey of consumer attitudes to food, nutrition and health. That survey showed EU consumers to be generally aware of what defines healthy eating (as evidenced by their definition of healthy eating) and perceived it as an important influence in food choice. Despite this, 69% of them felt no need to alter their diets, believing them to be already healthy enough.

Some results from the IEFS physical activity survey illustrate the wide geographical variability in attitudes towards physical activity and actual existing activity levels.

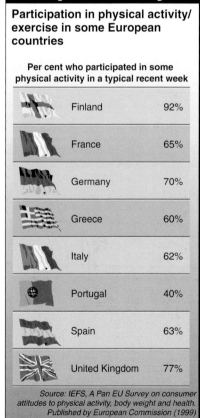

Physical activity

Participation in physical activity/exercise in some European countries

Per cent who participated in some physical activity in a typical recent week

	Country	%
	Finland	92%
	France	65%
	Germany	70%
	Greece	60%
	Italy	62%
	Portugal	40%
	Spain	63%
	United Kingdom	77%

Source: IEFS, A Pan EU Survey on consumer attitudes to physical activity, body weight and health. Published by European Commission (1999)

Finns rank physical activity as the most important influence on health, while Greeks rank it seventh. Such positive attitudes towards physical activity were reflected by the 92% of Finns participating in some physical activity versus just 60% of Greeks. The high level of awareness of the health benefits of physical activity together with the high participation rates may well reflect recent concerted efforts to increase population levels of physical activity in Finland.

Despite the huge variation in attitudes and activity levels between Finland and Greece, a similar proportion of consumers in both countries believe that their level of physical activity is sufficient. When compared to the Finns, the Greeks seem a degree over-optimistic. Over-optimism and complacency towards diet and physical activity represents one of the biggest challenges for those trying to stem the growing rise in obesity. Nonetheless, the Finnish data in this survey suggests that such a challenge can be met and that their promotional efforts to improving diet and increasing physical activity appear to be successful. This is encouraging for those involved in similar promotional efforts throughout the rest of Europe.

Data from this survey, the obstacles, the benefits and consumers' stage of readiness towards becoming more physically active, will help develop more focused strategies targeted at specific subgroups in the population and taking into account socio-demographic and geographical factors.

Reference
1. IEFS, *A Pan EU survey on consumer attitudes to physical activity, body weight and health*. Published by European Commission (1999)

Nutrition facts on adolescence

Energy and nutrient requirements

Growth and development are rapid during the teenage years, and the demand for energy and most nutrients is relatively high. This demand differs between boys and girls: boys need more protein and energy than girls due to their greater growth spurt.

The growth spurt usually begins around 10 years of age in girls and 12 years of age in boys. In both sexes, an average of 23cm is added to height and 20-26kg to weight. Before adolescence, both girls and boys have an average of 18% body fat. During adolescence this increases to about 28% in girls and decreases to about 15% in boys.

One way to obtain sufficient energy is by the consumption of frequent snacks as well as meals. However, some adolescents eat more than they need and may become overweight, especially if they are inactive. It is better to try to prevent obesity than to encourage strict dieting in this age group. Encouraging a healthy lifestyle is therefore of prime importance during these years. Good habits practised now will be likely to benefit their health for the rest of their lives.

There is an increasing tendency for teenagers, particularly girls, to control their weight by unsuitable methods such as smoking or adopting very low energy diets. Restriction of many food items can lead to nutrient deficiencies and problems in later life. During adolescence iron requirements increase to help with growth and muscle development.

After menstruation begins, girls need more iron than boys to replace menstrual losses. It is thought that about 4% of adolescent boys and 17% of adolescent girls are anaemic. Those who start a poorly planned vegetarian diet or are slimming may be particularly at risk. Consumption of breakfast cereals and/or bread which have been fortified with iron is important, together with food or drink containing vitamin C, e.g. fruit juice. However, many adolescents do not eat breakfast, so these foods could be encouraged as snacks instead.

The rapid increase in bone mass in adolescents means that they require more calcium than adults. Boys should aim for 1000mg per day and girls for 800mg.

Dietary habits

There has been a lot of concern about the eating habits of adolescents in recent years. A survey carried out in the UK in 1983 showed that the main sources of energy of adolescents were bread, chips, milk, biscuits, meat products, cake and puddings. While this resulted in a diet that was high in fat, the intake of many other nutrients appeared to be within the acceptable range. However, iron, calcium and riboflavin intakes were unacceptably low in the sample of girls. Girls ate more fruit and vegetables than boys, while boys ate more chips, milk, breakfast cereals and baked beans than girls.

In addition, a study carried out in 1986/7, which looked at the eating habits of teenage smokers, found that girls had significantly lower intakes of vitamins A, C, some B vitamins and fibre than those who did not smoke and also had the lowest intake of vegetables.

Eating disorders

Anorexia nervosa and bulimia nervosa are psychological illnesses which may affect young women and adolescent girls, and increasingly adolescent boys. Anorexia nervosa is the refusal to eat enough to maintain a normal body weight and an intense fear of gaining weight or becoming fat even though the individual is of normal weight or underweight. Sufferers are of the impression that they are fat and often see themselves as being fat even though they are obviously underweight. Many anorexics exercise vigorously or use slimming pills to keep their weight as low as possible. Along with a very low body weight, female anorexics often stop menstruating. This can have a serious effect on their ability to optimise the strength of their skeleton.

Bulimia nervosa sufferers are also obsessed with the fear of gaining weight. There is a recurring pattern of binge eating followed by self-induced vomiting. The foods eaten tend to be high in carbohydrate and fat. Sufferers may also use large quantities of laxatives, slimming pills or strenuous exercise to control their weight. Many bulimics have poor teeth due to regular vomiting. Vomit is acidic and can erode teeth.

No-gym generation

State students may turn into couch potatoes, heads warn

State schools are in danger of turning out a generation of couch potato children because they have so few facilities and so little time for PE and games, head teachers warned yesterday.

Few primaries have a gym, let alone a swimming pool or tennis court – all of which are standard in the private sector, it was claimed. Some do not even have a playground.

In too many cases, facilities on offer are 'not much better than in a banana republic,' according to the heads' spokesman David Hart. In addition, he said, staff are under such pressure to raise academic standards that they are reducing the hours devoted to sport and fitness. The result, increasingly, will be British failure at international level in almost every sport.

The problem needs urgent Government action, said Mr Hart, general secretary of the National Association of Head Teachers.

'There is enormous national yearning for us to win the World Cup,' he added. 'When are we going to have a female in the top ten rankings in tennis to match Tim Henman and Greg Rusedski?

'We have a yearning to be the top cricket nation in the world and to win the World Cup in rugby. We must not ignore that yearning on the part of the British public. But it will not be fulfilled if we skew the whole debate on to Premier League football academies, which are only designed to benefit Premier League clubs, and a small number of specialist schools.'

The NAHT carried out a survey of 2,126 schools and found that 94 per cent of primaries had no gym, 92 per cent had no swimming pool, and 97 per cent had no tennis court.

Almost every primary had a hall for PE lessons, but it was also used for assemblies, drama classes, meals, and exams. Twenty-five per cent of primaries said they had inadequate time for PE as a result.

By Tony Halpin,
Education Correspondent

Twenty-five per cent also had no access to a public pool. Of those which did, 80 per cent had to pay for its use, with most relying on parents to do so. The survey found that 51 per cent of primaries had to share playing fields. Among primary and secondary schools, 16 per cent lacked funds to maintain them properly.

Almost every primary had a hall for PE lessons, but it was also used for assemblies, drama classes, meals, and exams

Seventy-five per cent said it was difficult to produce sports teams at weekends – either because teachers were unwilling, or because pupils were unavailable. Secondary schools also reported many more children working part-time jobs at weekends.

Nearly 50 per cent of primaries and 39 per cent of secondaries also had trouble raising teams on weekdays.

Fit and healthy children are happier and able to concentrate more on their lessons, said Mr Hart – but this is being threatened by a 'utilitarian Gradgrind curriculum'.

Overall, PE and sports activities had 'decreased significantly' in the past two years in more than 40 per cent of primaries and 21 per cent of secondary and special schools, and fitness levels are now at crisis point, he added.

'Nothing illustrates the yawning gap between the affluent independent sector and the "strapped for cash" State sector quite so starkly.

'Unless the Government is prepared to push this issue to the top of the political agenda, we will see this country's youngsters turn into a generation of couch potatoes.'

But Schools Minister Charles Clarke insisted the Government is giving 'the highest priority' to sport in schools. It had established 34 specialist sports colleges, and a 'significant proportion' of the £180 million of national lottery money available to schools from April would be used to boost after-school sports.

© The Daily Mail
March, 1999

The joy of exercise

We are now a nation of couch potatoes, and a decline of PE in schools is to blame. Rubbish, says Tom McNab, school games never made anybody fit

Scarcely a week seems to pass without the appearance of yet another doom-laden report claiming that our children are couch potatoes, that 20 per cent of our population is obese and that heart disease is assuming the proportions of the Great Plague.

Almost invariably, a physical educationist then pops up to tell us that this relates to the decline in the volume of physical education in the school curriculum. For, the argument runs, since it now amounts to a mere hour's activity a week, it is hardly surprising that our children are fat, that the middle-aged are dropping like flies, and that our prospects at the Sydney Olympics are dim.

On the surface, this seems a plausible argument. But let's first dispose of the relationship between international sports performance and curricular PE. In 1950-60, the Golden Age of PE (when after-school sport was also at its peak), our World Cup soccer team was beaten by the US, our only 1952 Olympic gold medal winner was a horse, and British athletes languished behind those from Poland, France and Finland. Now, at a time of decreasing PE and after-school sport, we are ahead in all those areas and in many others, such as rowing, judo and swimming.

The fact is that international success has never had much to do with the volume of curricular PE. Rather, it has always related to well-structured coaching and competitive programmes from club to international level. For, though it is important to have a solid recreational base, this is now far less dependent on curricular school experience of sport than it was in the immediate post-war period.

So what about curricular PE's contribution to health and fitness? Alas PE, even at its peak volume, contributed little to children's fitness levels. I well remember my own school PE experience under a teacher reckoned to be one of Scotland's leading physical educationists. We had a couple of periods a week of barren Ling-based gymnastics, swinging our arms back and forward, and jumping on and off vaulting horses. There was a double period of games, when the 40-strong class was divided into two soccer teams to battle it out. When gymnastics gave way to swimming, a lesson consisted of the swimmers ploughing up and down the pool and the non-swimmers performing futile dry-land exercises, dedicated only to drowning. None of the above had much impact on fitness.

Take away the pleasure, and for most children there is no point to games, sport and exercise

---

Whatever fitness we possessed in those far-off days came not from curricular PE but from a Spartan post-war diet and vast volumes of walking and street play. I would reckon our weekly calorific output of street play at about 4,000 calories, over 1lb in body weight. It is no wonder that we were slim. Alas, this Golden Age of PE was one in which 52 per cent of our population smoked cigarettes, when more than two million people worked in noxious heavy industries, and when less than 1 per cent of adults engaged in sport and exercise.

For, believe it or not, now is the Golden Age of exercise. Indeed, there appears to be an inverse correlation between the volume of curricular PE and adult levels of vigorous physical activity. For, as curricular PE has decreased, the level of adult involvement in exercise has grown, with two million adults now members of private fitness clubs and the same number belonging to their local authority equivalents.

In my youth, any adult taking part in vigorous sport would have been considered eccentric. The range of sports has now gone far beyond conventional team games, with the population taking part in activities as diverse as indoor rock-climbing, tae kwon do and line-dancing.

The core of the problem about physical education is not lack of time, but rather the unwillingness to admit that physical activity, though it undoubtedly has an impact on children's characters, is essentially about pleasure. Take away the pleasure, and for most children there is no point to games, sport and exercise.

Alas PE, desperate to be at top table, has since the last war set its sails to prevailing educational winds, keen to prove on the one hand its cognitive content and on the other its contribution to the development of body and spirit. Thus for many without physical talent PE has tended to be a joyless experience.

The main dynamic in the growth of sport and exercise in the past couple of decades has come from local authorities, governing bodies and the private sector. Many physical educationists would argue that these agencies have fed on the interest created by curricular PE. This is true only in the correlative sense, in that every child is required by law to experience curricular PE, but most sports studies show that the main influence in participation is the parent, often the mother. For what possible attraction can there be for those lacking physical talent in a gymnasium equipped with the vaulting horse, balancing beams and wallbars of the mid-19th century? What joy can there be in sodden, windswept winter games fields for any but the physically gifted?

The old PE laid claim to physical

development without making the slightest attempt to test its claims. Similarly, modern PE claims to touch on almost every aspect of the human condition, with little supporting evidence. Here, I would insert one caveat – several studies show that primary school PE provides a stimulus to academic work. So what is the future for physical education? In the state sector, it is declining rapidly, though there are vigorous campaigns to buttress it through such agencies as the Youth Sport Trust. Only in the heavily funded independent schools, where curricular and extra-curricular sport are seamless, and in

rare examples in the state sector, does the subject show any health.

A radical change is needed in both quantity and quality. First, we need a new breed of PE teacher, men and women who are specialists in a narrow range of sports, employed by local education authorities and bought in by schools. Second, we need early starts and later finishes (8.30am and 4.30pm), so that at least once a week each child will secure two hours of enjoyable physical activity.

In the end, it is a question of curricular PE returning to the roots of sport, which have always lain in

joy, in pleasure. For the subject has, over the years, tried to distance itself from sweaty, competitive sport, preferring to indulge in untested claims about cognition and character.

The curricular PE of the 21st century must be firmly rooted in pleasure, for the test of the discipline must always be what those who are not physically gifted derive from it. If we get that right, all else will surely follow.

Telly turns children into tubbies

Overweight children can shed pounds by watching less television, according to a study published yesterday.

Children involved in a one-year effort to cut down their viewing gained significantly less body fat than a control group of their peers. The study, conducted by Stanford University, California, and said to be the first experimental test of the television-obesity link in school-children, found that children in the trial gained an average of two pounds less than children at the control school.

Dr Joel Killin, one of the research team, told the Paediatric Academic Societies annual meeting in San Francisco yesterday that this was the first time significant evidence had been produced to support the long-suspected television-weight link. The author, Dr Thomas Robinson, said the pilot study of 192 eight and nine-year-olds at two elementary schools in San Jose, California, was unique because it reduced viewing of television, videos and video games without promoting alternatives. He said: 'As a result, we were able to isolate the effects of these media alone.'

American children now spend, on average, more than four hours a day watching television and videos

*By Roger Highfield,
Science Editor*

or playing video games, so that only sleep consumes a larger share of the average child's day. Television-reduction lessons began by encouraging children to keep track of how much time they spent viewing. The children were then encouraged to go 10 days without television – a feat that two-thirds accomplished – before setting limits of seven hours of television per week.

Children attending the school that had received the television-reduction lessons did cut their viewing by about one-third to one-fourth, compared with their peers. They also showed a significantly

smaller increase in waist size, waist-to-hip ratio and body mass index, a measure of weight adjusted for height. However, the two schools did not differ in consumption of high-fat foods, amount of moderate-to-vigorous exercise, or physical fitness.

To account for the weight difference, Dr Robinson said one possibility was that the children who cut back on television were performing more low-level activities – more energetic than simply sitting still but less energetic than walking. The difference may also stem from changes in the number of meals the kids ate in front of the television. The children at the trial school significantly decreased the number of meals they ate while viewing.

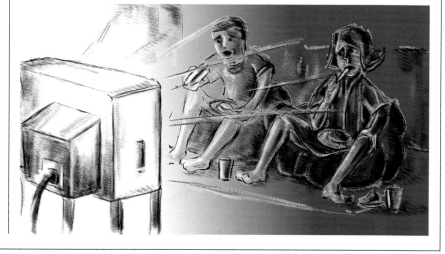

Nutrition facts on obesity

Obesity

Body weight is affected by energy intake from food and energy output, i.e. energy needed for basic body processes (such as keeping the heart beating) and for physical activity. If a person regularly gets even a little more energy from food than they need, they may start to gain weight and eventually become overweight. Extra energy from food and drink is mostly stored as fat. Balancing energy intake and output to maintain a healthy weight has many benefits.

Measuring body weight

Comparing weight against height is a quick and easy way of finding out if someone is a healthy weight for their height. A more useful way to judge whether a person is overweight is to work out body mass index (BMI). The BMI values below are for adults, i.e. when growth has stopped.

BMI is worked out by the formula:weight (in kilograms) divided by height x height (in metres)

The BMI can be compared with the following ranges:

Below 20   Underweight
20-25   Acceptable
25-30   Overweight
30-40   Obese
Over 40   Very obese

For example, an adult woman weighing 60kg who is 1.6m tall has a BMI of 23.4. She is therefore a healthy weight.

How common is obesity?

Obesity is common in North America, Australasia and Europe. It also occurs, but is less common, in developing countries. In 1996, 45% of men and 34% of women in England were overweight. A further 16% and 18% respectively were obese. It is likely that the incidence is similar in other parts of the UK. Obesity tends to be more common among people aged 40-60 years and those from lower income groups. Today, more people are obese than ever before.

It is normal to store fat during growth, particularly during infancy and adolescence. It is therefore difficult to measure obesity in children. The number of children who are very much heavier than would be expected for their height is about 2% in primary school children and 10% in secondary school children.

Overweight and health

People who are obese are more likely to suffer from coronary heart disease, adult onset diabetes, gallstones, arthritis, high blood pressure and some types of cancer. People who have their extra weight around the middle – 'apple shaped' – are at more risk of some of these diseases than those who have most of the extra weight around their hips and thighs – 'pear shaped'. Men tend to be more 'apple shaped' whereas women tend to be more 'pear shaped'. People who are very overweight find it more difficult to be physically active and this may add to their health problems. Most of the health problems associated with obesity are removed once the extra weight is lost. Although people who smoke cigarettes tend to weigh less than people who do not smoke, the risks from smoking are greater than those of being obese.

The role of exercise

Many people in the UK have very inactive lifestyles – few people have physically active jobs or do significant amounts of exercise out of work. Lack of activity is an important factor in the increasing incidence of obesity. Walking or cycling instead of using a car, going to exercise classes and taking part in team sports such as football or basketball can all help a person maintain a healthy body weight by increasing energy output. Any form of activity or exercise that people enjoy should be encouraged. People who are already overweight are usually encouraged to become more active as well as reducing the amount of energy provided by their diet.

The role of food

All diets containing more energy than a person needs can cause weight gain. But, because fat provides just over twice as much energy per gram (37 kJ/g) as carbohydrate (17 kJ/g), a diet high in fat can make over-consumption more likely. Foods high in complex carbohydrates (starchy foods) may be more filling than foods high in fat. It may also be that excess dietary fat is more easily converted to body fat than excess carbohydrate or protein. Alcohol is also rich in energy (29 kJ/g).

Losing weight

If someone is obese, they will usually need advice from their doctor or dietician about a suitable weight-reducing diet. This can be a good opportunity for someone to make general improvements to their diet. Special slimming products are not necessary. Preventing obesity is important, as dieting is difficult and often fails. Children who are very overweight are not put on slimming diets but are encouraged to become more active and, if appropriate, choose a more balanced diet.

Plump but not obese

Being overweight, but not obese (BMI 25-30), is not a risk to health but people in this range are encouraged not to put on any more weight and to ensure that they are exercising regularly and making sensible dietary choices.

In many countries, there are cultural pressures for people to be slim. Many people try to lose weight even though they are in the normal weight range for their height or only slightly plump. Unnecessary slimming is not advised, as this may lead to a person becoming underweight, and in severe cases may lead to development of an eating disorder, e.g. anorexia nervosa.

• The above information is an extract from the web site of the British Nutrition Foundation (BNF), which can be found on www.nutrition.org.uk/ or see page 42 for postal address details.

Fast food facts

The Fast Food Fact File gives you the facts about some popular fast foods, so you can make the most of healthier choices. But first a few basic facts about healthy eating.

A healthy diet is made up mostly of foods like bread, potatoes, pasta and rice with plenty of salad, veggies and fruit. If your meal contains plenty of these, chances are you're well on your way to a healthy choice.

Milk, dairy foods, meat, fish or their alternatives like beans, peas and nuts are also important. However, aim for low-fat cheeses, lean meats and fish and watch out for things which have been fried, particularly where they're crumbed or coated.

Foods containing fat and foods containing sugar can be part of a healthy diet, but only if you eat them in relatively small amounts.

Burgers, chicken, kebabs

The amount of fat your burger contains partly depends on how it's cooked. Grilled burgers can actually be quite lean, but burgers fried on a griddle will contain a lot more fat.

Lamb and chicken shish kebabs contain less fat than a kofta or doner kebab because they're made from leaner meat. A typical shish kebab, with salad and pitta bread, contains around 10 grams of fat whereas a doner may contain around 50 grams of fat!

A skinless chicken shish kebab in a pitta with loads of salad is lean and filling. Give the chips a miss and you've got a balanced healthy meal.

Any coated and deep-fried foods will be relatively high in fat. The best advice is probably to eat them and thoroughly enjoy them, just not too often!

Most of the fat in chicken is just beneath the skin; remove the skin and you remove a lot of the fat.

Frying any food in batter or breadcrumbs means it will absorb fat. Because of this, grilled or oven-cooked chicken, especially skinless chicken, is a healthier choice than coated, deep-fried chicken.

In chicken restaurants the best option is usually grilled skinless chicken served in a bun. Add plenty of salad to get the balance right.

In some places chicken burgers are coated and fried. But served in a bun with relish instead of mayonnaise, they're still a healthier choice than having several pieces of fried chicken served with thin-cut chips or fries.

Three pieces of fried chicken served with thin-cut chips or fries contains almost 80 grams of fat, a coated chicken burger in a bun around 30 grams of fat and a burger made with grilled skinless chicken, and relish in place of mayonnaise, around 5 grams of fat.

Fish and chips

The thicker the chip, the less fat it absorbs during cooking

Weight for weight, homemade thick-cut chips contain around half the fat of thinner-cut French fries. Homemade thick-cut chips usually contain about 7% fat. French fries usually contain around 15% fat.

Oven chips are a good option if you're cooking chips at home. Usually they contain less than 5% fat.

Fish and chips are still very popular. A recent survey by the HEA showed that nearly 6 in every 10 people regularly visit the chippy.

Fish has a reputation of being healthy, and with potatoes makes a filling nutritious meal. Fried in batter though, it can contain a lot of fat. So have some bread or ask for mushy peas or baked beans to fill you up and get the balance right.

Ask what fat or oil your local chippy uses for frying. If they use unsaturated oils at the right temperature, your fish and chips will contain less fat and be healthier.

Although they are thickly cut, chip-shop chips usually contain about 12% fat. This is because they're often part cooked in advance and then 'refreshed' by quickly frying them again, when they are ready to be served.

Pizza and pasta

Italians know all about healthy eating. Their 'Mediterranean' diet contains plenty of fruit, veg and fish, and lots of starchy food like pasta, bread and pizza bases. These are excellent foods to fill up on.

Thick-crust pizzas are a healthier choice than thin-crust pizzas. They're more filling, so you'll eat proportionally more base and less topping, and have less room for the tiramisu.

Pasta is very good for you, and very filling. Pasta has had a reputation for being high in fat, but it isn't the pasta that's the culprit, it's the cream and butter-laden sauces that go with it!

A simple tomato sauce is a traditional low-fat pasta topping. For a healthier option tomato-based sauces made with vegetables, fish or lean meat are the ones to go for, instead of the butter, cream and cheese-based sauces.

Sandwiches, jackets

A medium baking potato weighs about 180 grams and contains less than 1 gram of fat. The same potato would make 6 bags of crisps, which would contain around 10 grams of fat each!

All bread, especially wholemeal, is good for you. A lot of the fat in sandwiches can come from butter, margarine, mayonnaise, or oil-based dressing. Why not ask for relishes, lemon juice, or black pepper instead?

Potatoes are an excellent source of starch, and if eaten with the skins are a good source of fibre.

Keep fatty baked potato fillings like cheese or sour cream as a treat and when you do have them, try not to have butter as well.

Don't forget there are plenty of sandwich fillings which are healthier choices e.g., lean meats like ham, beef, pork, turkey, chicken, chicken tikka; fish like prawns, tuna without mayonnaise, sardines; sliced egg, cottage cheese and Edam.

Good choices for vegans include fillings based on beans or chick peas, such as humus, curried chick peas or bean salads. Peanut butter and tahini paste are good sources of protein for vegans, but are relatively high in fat, so go easy on these and ask for plenty of salad for a balanced filling.

Junk food is 'health risk to British children'

By Celia Hall,
Medical Editor

British children are among the unhealthiest in Europe, affected by poor diet even before they are born, a report said yesterday.

Britain comes 18th in a Unicef list of childhood deaths between birth and five, behind Japan, Germany and France – fellow G8 countries – and even below Slovenia. It is on a par with Ireland and New Zealand. According to the World Health Organisation, Britain had the highest rate of babies born below normal birth weight (under 5.5lb) in Europe. It ranked with Albania with seven per cent of babies born underweight.

Dr James Appleyard, honorary consultant paediatrician and chairman of a British Medical Association working group that has produced a study called *Growing up in Britain*, said: 'Children in Britain in social class five are four times more likely to die from accidents than those in class one.

'They have twice the rate of long-standing illness, they are smaller at birth and shorter in height. They get a relatively poor deal. In other words we are programming our children at that age for a lifetime of problems.'

He called for an end to the 'turf wars' between government departments and independent agencies to ensure that the interests of children became paramount. 'Health policy makers need to justify placing children's services so low on the agenda.'

The report shows that among the British children who do not survive beyond the age of four, 22 per cent die from injury or poisoning; 20 per cent from birth abnormalities; 13 per cent from cancer, and 12 per cent from diseases of the nervous system.

Dr Appleyard said: 'We are failing to put children at the centre of our priorities and we are punishing them for the problems and inadequacies of their parents. The first five years of life are absolutely crucial to the development of children's

'Families on restricted incomes with children . . . are buying food that they know children will like, regardless of quality, because it isn't wasted'

bodies, minds and personalities. Deprivation in early life causes lifelong damage, delinquency and despair.'

Dr Vivienne Nathanson, the head of health policy and research for the BMA, said: 'The fact is that if you have families on restricted incomes with children, they are buying food that they know children will like, regardless of quality, because it isn't wasted. Let's say to the supermarkets, start advertising foods that are healthy for children in a way that makes it more fun for them to be eating fresh fruit and vegetables instead of junk food.'

Encouraging breast feeding to improve health and nutrition is another positive measure urged in the report. The BMA is calling on the Government to appoint an independent commissioner for children to oversee child health policies and for the Chief Medical Officer to produce an annual report on children's health.

Martin Barnes, director of the Child Poverty Action Group, said: 'The CPAG calls on the Government to reverse the planned 1p basic rate tax cut. The £2.8 billion it would lose in revenue should instead be invested in tackling child poverty, including health inequalities.'

Army caves in to the fast food invasion

By James Clark

They say an army marches on its stomach. But British soldiers may well end up waddling into war if plans to revolutionise their diet go ahead.

The Ministry of Defence wants to let fast-food chains such as McDonald's, Burger King and Harry Ramsden's infiltrate junior ranks' messes.

It sees the move as a way of making a military career more attractive to young people, while saving money.

Senior officers, however, fear the daily temptation of burgers, chips and fizzy drinks will prove irresistible, leaving troops less than fighting fit, while dieticians are speaking of a 'nutritional disaster' in the making.

The Naafi, which has fed the forces for 79 years, has been working on what it calls its Vision 2000 since New Labour's Strategic Defence Review called for new ways to make Army life appealing to recruits. It wants to buy franchises in the fast-food chains, and issue troops with 'smart cards' to pay for their meals as they eat. At present soldiers pay a subsidised monthly mess bill.

The MoD claims the change will help give 'a modern, village feel to base life', with the mess acting as the 'village centre'.

But senior officers have long warned that many rookies are too unfit to complete their training, thanks to years of soft living and a diet of fatty food. One said: 'Any army which had been eating a diet of hamburgers for a few years is not going to march very far at all. We have enough of a problem getting the right calibre of recruit without doing our best to turn the ones we do get into couch potatoes.'

And a Parachute Regiment major said: 'We all like a burger every now and then, but my soldiers could not do the job they are trained for if that was their daily diet. Paratroopers have to be extremely fit indeed.'

A spokesman for the British Dietetic Association, Lyndel Costain, described the proposal as 'stupid in the extreme', saying: 'A burger for novelty every now and then is fine, but to eat them all the time without essential vegetables and fruit would be terrible.

'Soldiers are like sportsmen, in that they burn up lots of energy in their day and they need a carefully planned diet to do it.'

Senior officers, however, fear the daily temptation of burgers, chips and fizzy drinks will prove irresistible, leaving troops less than fighting fit

The Naafi recently displayed a mock-up of a new-look mess at St Omer Barracks, Aldershot. Its business director Simon Harris said: 'This sort of thing is what soldiers go out and spend their money on when they are not in their messes. Bright signs and promotional material will change the whole feel of soldiers' dining rooms and make them look like a "food theatre".

He stressed salad bars and 'big pan cooking' would be available.

And the MoD said that while troops would be free to choose what they ate, research showed that healthy foods such as chicken and milk were among the most popular on military menus.

However Miss Costain replied that given a choice, many young people preferred junk food to other restaurant fare, and soldiers would be no different.

And why the rest of us are lazy and out of shape

Britain is becoming a nation of overweight people who don't do enough to keep fit and eat unhealthy food, a report said yesterday.

It revealed that almost 40 per cent admit they do no weekly exercise and just as many say they are too fat for their own liking.

Worse, only 10 per cent of Britons eat enough fresh fruit and vegetables – most having less than three helpings a day instead of the five recommended by nutrition experts.

Women are much less likely than men to exercise and are more likely to think they weigh too much.

About 45 per cent say they are fat compared to 33 per cent of men.

Health campaigners are also alarmed at the rise in the number of heavyweight children to some 33 per cent of the under-16s. They blame playing computer games instead of sport and parents who drive pupils to school thus depriving them of a vital daily walk or cycle ride.

The Gallup poll, commissioned by the BBC, launched a drive to persuade us to improve our habits. Fiona Pitcher, of the BBC's Fighting Fat, Fighting Fit campaign, said: 'There's no such thing as a quick-fix diet that works.

'We want to encourage people to make small changes that make a big difference.'

Experts believe more exercise and eating more fruit and vegetables is better than dieting in the long run. They say just getting up to change TV channels can shed 2lbs a year. But Britons remain optimistic that all is not lost, with over half making a New Year resolution to do more exercise in 1999.

Children's diet

Parents are unconcerned about children's current diet whilst children say healthy eating is sensible . . . but boring

The LACA School Meals Survey was conducted by the Gallup Organisation between 10 February and 25 March 1999. A representative sample of 1,200 children aged 8-16 years of age and 1000 parents with children 8-16 years of age living in their household throughout Scotland, England and Wales were interviewed by telephone.

The new Gallup Survey into attitudes towards school meals and healthy eating which was commissioned by the Local Authority Caterers' Association (LACA) reveals that, contrary to the widespread concerns of health experts, well over a third of parents (37%) are not at all concerned or worried about their children's current diet

Despite the fact that almost half of parents (46%) consider the evening meal they provide their children to be high in nutritional value, they believe that understanding the nutritional values of different foods is less important to their children's health in adult life. Only three in five (58%) rated it as very important compared to other aspects such as healthy lifestyle (79%), balanced diet (79%) and taking regular gentle exercise (76%) which were all ranked very important by a greater proportion of parents.

Parents rely on schools for discipline, diet and social skills

Although, maybe understandably, over half of parents (53%) rely completely on the school for the provision of basic education, a surprising quarter of parents say they also rely totally on the school to teach their children discipline and social skills (27% and 23% respectively) and for their knowledge of physical fitness (26%).

Disproving the belief that traditional family meal times are in decline, nearly two-thirds of parents (65%) claim that their children eat an evening meal at home at the table. Yet, disturbingly, nearly a quarter of parents (21%) are allowing their children to eat their evening meal off a tray on their laps and nearly two out of three children (39%) say they are more likely to eat with a knife and fork in school than out

With the pressures of modern living, parents say they not only rely completely on schools to educate their children, but one in five (22%) say they depend totally on the school to also provide them with a balanced diet. Three out of five (60%) agreed that school meals play a vital role in children's diets and nearly half of parents (45%) believe that school meals are now better than they were in their own schooldays. Around four out of five (78%) ate school meals themselves and four out of five children (84%) who eat school meals today like them (41% a lot).

Total meal provision at school?

The Survey also reveals evidence of a growing demand from parents for total meal provision by the school. With both parents working full time and struggling to provide meals at either end of their children's school day, well in excess of a third of parents (39%) said that they would like the option of breakfast being served in school and just under a quarter (21%) would like to see an evening meal served after lessons finish. Nearly half (44%) of children agreed that they would like breakfast at school, with girls (47%) slightly more in favour than boys (41%). Over a third (36%) would also opt for an evening meal after school with the most enthusiasm coming from the younger age group (46% of 8-10-year-olds; 34% of 11-13-year-olds; 29% of 14-16-year-olds).

However, despite their dependency on schools for their children's personal development and well-being, the financial strains on parents' pockets is such today that two out of five parents (41%) report not giving their children any lunch money. Paradoxically parents in the so-called 'affluent south' are less likely to give lunch money than their counterparts elsewhere in the country (47% vs. 37% in the rest of Britain).

A similar picture is painted by the children interviewed with one-third (32%) saying they do not receive any lunch money. Amongst those who never eat school meals, well over half (58%) do not receive any lunch money. Of those children who eat a school meal every day, three in ten (30%) qualify for free meals.

Although the majority of children who do receive lunch money say that they always spend it on their school meal (59%), a third (33%) admit to spending it on other things.

Healthy eating sensible but boring

Whilst the Survey clearly demonstrates that children on the whole seem well aware these days of what is and what is not healthy, the most popular items purchased with lunch money continue to be sweets (32%) followed by chocolate (12%) or crisps (12%). Temptation it seems continues to quash good sense.

Although the healthy eating messages have got through with children readily able to identify which foods and drinks are healthy, they are disregarding them. Despite the fact that fruit is rated as very healthy by four out of five (81%) followed by salad (75%) and then milk (65%) none of the foods and drinks considered very healthy made it into children's top ten favourite school meals.

Whilst an almost unanimous nine out of ten children believe that their friends would say healthy eating was 'sensible' (89%) and three-quarters (74%) agreed that it was 'clever', one in five children (21%) still admit that chips would be their favourite choice for a school meal with burgers in fifth place. However, when asked to consider how healthy foods and drinks were, chips, burgers and fizzy drinks were the most likely to be rated as not at all healthy (15%, 14% and 17% respectively). Perhaps the key to unlocking this contradictory dilemma lies in the fact that two out of five (40%) said that their friends find healthy eating 'boring'. A challenge clearly exists for health educationalists, school caterers and food producers alike.

The 'cool factor' also varies dramatically between the sexes. Boys are more likely to say that their peers think healthy eating is 'boring' (46% vs. 34% girls) whilst girls are likely to say that their peers think it's cool (55% vs. 48% boys).

It does appear that wherever healthy eating is taught in the classroom, children are more enthusiastic about lunch time itself. 71% of children said they enjoyed it a lot compared to 59% of those who miss out on this type of education. Although three-quarters of children in the Survey said they are taught about healthy eating, it is the middle age group which gets the higher priority with 83% of 11-13-year-olds being taught the subject compared to 71% of 14-16-year-old and 68% of 8-10-year-olds. Starting nutritional education young could be critical to forming good dietary habits which last a lifetime.

- A summary of the findings from the 1999 Local Authority Caterers' Association (LACA) *School Meals Survey*, conducted amongst 1,000 parents and 1,200 children aged 8-16 years of age by the Gallup Organisation.

LACA is the professional body representing 800 catering managers who provide services to all sectors of local authorities.

© LACA
April, 1999

Additional findings

Three out of five (59%) of parents say that one or more of their children eat school meals. Parents report that two out of three (67%) of those who do eat school meals, do so every day. This represents a total of two in five parents (39%) saying that their children eat school meals every day.

Two out of three (66%) of the children surveyed eat school meals, of those who eat school meals, over half (58%) do so every day. This represents well over a third (38%) of all children eating school meals every day.

The typical spend for a school meal by parents and children is £1.20. Parents claim a spend of £1.39 by their 11-13-year-olds although children in this age group say they actually spend £1.20 on their school meal. Similarly, parents claim a spend of £1.50 for 14-16-year-olds but this group says it spends a lower sum of £1.25 on a school meal.

Dinner ladies are still the children's favourite with about half of children (49%) giving the traditional dinner ladies' school meals service their vote!

Children's top ten favourite school meals are:
1. Chips
2. Pizza
3. Sausage/hot dog
4. Spaghetti/pasta
5. Burger
6. Jacket potato
7. Sandwich/Roll
8. Fish
9. Roast dinner
10. Curry (with rice or chips)

Although chips were the top choice of school meal with the majority of children (21%), children in the Midlands and Wales appear to be the 'chip kings' with 29% opting for this meal vs. 18% in Scotland/North and 19% in the South.

Children in Scotland and the North have a greater taste for sausages or hot dogs than children elsewhere (11% vs. 6% in the Midlands and Wales and 7% in the South); whilst children in the South appear to have more continental preferences, choosing spaghetti or pasta more than their counterparts in the Midlands and Wales (10% vs. 5% in the Midlands/Wales).

More children eat school meals in the Midlands, Wales, the North and Scotland than those in the South (68% vs. 62%).

Children in the North and Scotland are more in favour of breakfast and an evening meal being served in school than their southern counterparts (48% vs. 41% for breakfast/40% vs. 36% for an evening meal).

© LACA

Why being overweight can pile on the years

By Jenny Hope, Medical Correspondent

Being overweight can have the effect of adding more than six years to a person's age, hastening sickness and death, a study says.

The fatter someone is, the more likely they are to die earlier than they should, it warns.

The research was carried out in the US, which has some of the highest rates of obesity in the world – but Britain is catching up fast as the number of overweight adults soars.

In Britain, 20 per cent of women and 17 per cent of men are clinically obese and 45 per cent of men and 33 per cent of women are overweight, according to Department of Health figures.

The American study found that obesity increases the risk of death from natural causes for a man aged between 40 and 50 to that of a male 5.9 years older. The risk for an obese woman of the same age increases to that of a female 6.4 years older. 'The more obese a person is, the more years he or she artificially adds to his or her real age and the greater the chance of dying in any given year,' said Dr June Stevens, one of the authors of the report of the study in the *American Journal of Epidemiology*.

'If you are a man in his 70s and you are obese, you are taking on the death rate of men who are 3.5 years older than you are. An obese woman of the same age boosts her risk of premature death by 1.7 years.'

The researchers at the University of North Carolina defined obesity as a Body Mass Index (BMI) – weight in kilos divided by height in metres squared – of 30 or more.

That means a 6ft man should weigh no more than 15st 12lb and at 5ft 4in should stay below 12st 8lb. A BMI between 18.5 and 25 is considered ideal for adults and a typical catwalk model would have a BMI of about 18.

The study found that a 5ft 10in man aged between 30 and 44 faces a 20 per cent higher risk of death if he weighs 11st 12lb than if he weighs 20lb less. The researchers analysed the deaths of white men and women who had taken part in a cancer prevention study carried out from 1960 to 1972, but who had been healthy when alive.

None of the 62,000 men and 262,000 women had smoked, or had a history of heart disease, strokes or cancer. The researchers took account of age, education, physical activity and drinking.

Dr Susan Jebb, of the Medical Research Council's health and nutrition research centre at Cambridge, commented: 'You may be chronologically only 50 years old, but if you're obese then metabolically you're heading into your late 50s.

'The data is old, but it also means that it was collected before we had soaring levels of obesity in recent years. The problem building up is even worse, because people are getting fatter at a younger age, so advancing ill-health and disability will affect them sooner.

'The biggest mystery is why people, who cannot be unaware of the ill-effects of being fat, do not change their lifestyle.

'It's a mix of prevention and treatment. But if everyone decided they would not put on any more weight, never mind losing any, in ten years' time they would reap the benefits.

'It's not just a matter of food intake. Perhaps the most important element is physical inactivity. Anyone undertaking regular physical activity, whatever their weight, achieves a health rating that is younger than their years.

'The biggest benefit is moving from no physical activity to some. Just having one TV-free night a week, when you go for a walk instead, has real benefits.'

© *The Daily Mail*
August, 1999

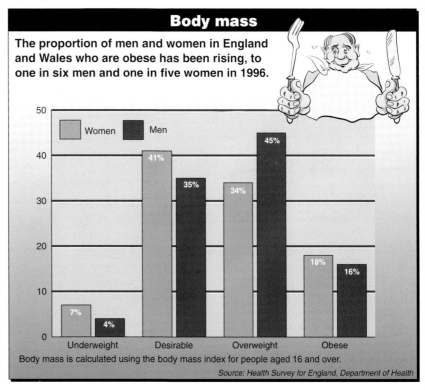

Body mass

The proportion of men and women in England and Wales who are obese has been rising, to one in six men and one in five women in 1996.

	Women	Men
Underweight	7%	4%
Desirable	41%	35%
Overweight	34%	45%
Obese	18%	16%

Body mass is calculated using the body mass index for people aged 16 and over.

Source: Health Survey for England, Department of Health

Can you be fit and fat?

In an age when overweight children are sent to slimming camp, the accepted wisdom is that you have to be thin to be healthy. But Jay Rayner weighs over 17 stone and has the heart of an athlete . . .

Earlier this year, during a routine medical check-up, my doctor told me I had 'an athlete's heart'. This was startling news. Up to that point, if a member of the Rayner family was told they had anything pertaining to an athlete, it was either because we had nicked it or because we had a fungal infection of the foot. And now here was I, able to boast that I had something in common with Linford Christie beyond a limb at each corner.

A healthy person's heart should run at between 68 and 72 beats per minute. Because they are stronger and therefore need to do less to achieve the same effect, athletes' hearts run slower. Mine was pumping at around 60. QED. I had become an athlete. Sort of.

It was not accidental. Four years ago, another newspaper sent me on a rigorous round of tests in an attempt to answer a simple question: can you be both fit and fat? There was no doubt I was the right man for the job. I have always been a large man. Hell, even when I was a boy there was enough of me to equal one large man. Had they existed at the time, I would have been a perfect candidate for the children's fat farm that opened last week in Leeds. But all I wanted then, despite the fact that I was as unmissable as a bus in a bike shed, was to go unnoticed. To be paraded before television cameras, as were the new recruits this week, would have destroyed me.

Happily, I was spared that experience. I lost the worst of the excess during adolescence, and came to accept that the rest was there simply because the Rayners are built that way, our bodies genetically designed to withstand the brutal winters of the Russian steppes whence we came. We are, as a result, perhaps a little over-engineered for the more temperate regions of London. In adulthood, my weight has settled down in a zone somewhere just to the north of 17 stone, much as Edinburgh is just to the north of London.

So, in the service of journalism, I went for a fitness check. At that point I swam occasionally. I reckoned I would have few problems. I was wrong. Boy, was I wrong. The hearty gentleman at the National Sports Medicine Institute who tested me sucked his teeth, shook his head and said lots of things about lowest quartiles and morbidity rates. He made me feel like I should start planning the dimensions of my coffin immediately.

Then he calculated my Body Mass Index. The BMI, which is your weight in kilograms divided by the square of your height in metres, is a way of measuring body size. A BMI of less than 20 and you are underweight. Between 20 and 25 is normal; 25 to 30 is overweight. Break the magic 30 and you are, like 20 per cent of women and 17 per cent of men in Britain, officially obese.

You've guessed it. Mine was more than 30. I was obese. Time, then, for exercise, lots of it. I joined a gym. I built up my stamina. I pushed weights. I pulled weights. I invited weights out for a movie and a light, low-fat supper afterwards.

I cannot claim that my gym-going was consistent. At times over the past four years it has been so inconsistent as to be merely the thing I did last autumn but don't do any more. But, in the past year, I have clambered back on to the step machine and gone for it. As a result, my doctor said I now had an athlete's heart. I decided it was time to return to the National Sports Medicine Institute for a second test. This time, when I asked the question 'can you be both fit and fat?', I was bloody well going to get the right answer.

I don't think it's any accident that I should decide to do this in July. When I was a teenager, the thought of the summer months terrified me. I knew that I would have to strip off to reveal vast acreages of this too too solid flesh. Pubertal girls used to envy me because I had larger breasts than them. With the passing of both some of the fat and the casual humiliations of adolescence, the fear and worry did ease but now, in the late Nineties, there is another threat: the newsstands.

Once it was only women who had to put up with magazines telling their readers that unless they lost weight, they would need a windbreak the size of Cardiff to hide behind on the beach to spare their embarrassment. Now the newsagents' shelves are bulging like a well-built bicep with titles telling men exactly the same thing.

There's *Men's Health* (recent coverline: 'Your New Body is Here! More Muscle, Less Fat'); there's ZM, 'For The Man Fit For Everything' (recent coverline: 'Get Bigger, Fitter Arms in 20 Mins'); there's even *Scientific American*, which is now available here and which dedicated its latest issue entirely to men and their bodies (coverline: 'Bulking Up. The Molecular Mystery of Muscle'). Every page of these titles is an admonishment, every photograph of every model a reminder of what will never be. The terrible thing is I found myself fascinated by just exactly how I could get bigger, fitter arms in 20 minutes. But then, as we now know, I have an athlete's heart. It is natural that I should be interested in these things.

And so to a basement room at the National Sports Medicine Institute, hard by St Bartholomew's Hospital in London, where a hearty, sun-kissed Australian by the name of David Bentley is preparing to put me through my paces. For around £50, depending on what tests you want, they'll do the same for you, although much of their work is with athletes. Clearly I had come to the right place, what with my heart and all. He looked at the results from my last test and did some non-committal nodding, before suggesting that I get on the scales.

The first shock of the day: I weighed five kilos, or a full 11 pounds, more than I did last time round. This meant my BMI had gone up rather than down. I was, according to the statistics, more obese rather than less. Then again, the BMI is poor when it comes to measuring people with a lot of muscle, because muscle weighs more than fat. Both Jonah Lomu and Mike Tyson would be classed as obese under the test. I muttered something to David about it being a blunt instrument. And he said: 'It still gives us a good idea of where we're at.' If that was the case, where we were at was a place I didn't want to be.

He measured my waist, my hips, my height and then my lung capacity. The latter, he said, was well above average. At last, a little encouragement. Next, he fired a small electric current though me to measure the fat content of my body. We would have to wait a day or so for all the calculations to be done. Finally, he wired me up to a heart monitor using three electrodes taped to my chest, and shoved a pipe in my mouth that would measure the amount of oxygen I was using. Then I clambered on to the treadmill.

The test is far simpler to describe than do. You walk at a steady rate of 6kph. Then, every couple of minutes,

the treadmill rises by an incline first of 5 per cent and then by 2.5 per cent every interval after that. You just – just! – have to keep going for as long as you can.

Last time I managed a pathetic eight minutes 45 seconds. I did reach my maximum heart rate – one of the points of the test – but that was all I reached. I tumbled off the treadmill a sweaty, snot-smeared wreck. This time it was clear that my efforts on the step machine and cross trackers had worked. I sailed through the eight-minute barrier, onwards through nine, 10, 11. Of course, I was still a sweaty, snot-smeared wreck, but it took longer to get there. Sweat dribbled down every crevice. My heart went into training to replace the rhythm section in a salsa band. My breathing

---

Are you fat? Are you fit?

How do you know if you're obese? Calculate your body mass index (BMI). Your BMI is your weight in kilograms divided by the square of your height in metres (1 pound = 0.45359 kilos; 1 inch = 0.0254 metres). A BMI of 20 to 25 is normal; over 30 shows that you are clinically obese.

How do you know if you're unfit?

The average person should be able to walk a mile in 12 minutes without getting out of breath.

How can you stay fit?

The minimum amount of exercise required to maintain average fitness is 20 minutes three times a week.

Where can you get more information?

The Sport and Exercise Performance Unit offers a range of tests and training, from simple skin fold measurements to Olympic-level endurance coaching. They can be reached at the National Sports Medicine Institute, Charterhouse Square, London EC1M 6BQ (0171 251 0583).

© The Guardian July, 1999

---

was as light and relaxed as a Caribbean hurricane, only less predictable. At 12 minutes and an incline of 15 per cent, David leaned over and – sweet mercy – stopped the machine.

The results of the test were promising. Four years ago I had managed to use only 33 millilitres of oxygen per kilo of body weight, when it should have been nearer 41.5. This time it was 38ml. Allowing for margins of error, I was apparently fit. My oxygen uptake had improved by more than 15 per cent, and I had worked out for longer.

The body fat content figures also seemed to me to be very reassuring. Last time, 32.5 per cent of my body had been fat. Now it was 29.9 per cent. Given that my weight had risen, it meant all of that increase – and more besides – had to be pure muscle. I calculated the extra muscle at one stone three pounds. My waist and hip measurements had dropped, which made sense: muscle is more compact than fat. I had, it seemed, sculpted myself into Jay 'the body' Rayner. That's me.

David was having none of it. My body shape, he said, had 'changed minimally'. Bastard. I argued with him. Body fat down. Weight up. It had to be muscle. He invoked margins of error. 'If you want to be fit, I would advise you to lose weight,' he said, although, being Australian, it came out sounding like a question rather than an imperative.

I had, inadvertently, arrived at an answer to that question, 'Can you be fit and fat?' That answer is no, because those who are doing the testing cannot bring themselves to allow such a thing. For them, fatness and fitness cannot exist in the same universe, let alone the same body. Well, my doctor and my ticker say otherwise. I have an athlete's heart. It's sitting here in my chest, and right now it's puttering away at a very healthy 56 beats a minute. I've worked for it, and now I've got it. Sure, it may be the only one of my organs that's athletic – but, you know, that one is good enough for me.

© The Guardian July, 1999

Nowadays the fats really do add up

More and more of us are becoming overweight, yet nobody is sure why. A new report helps dispel the myths

By Sanjida O'Connell

Fat is an alarming issue. A fifth of men and women in this country are clinically obese. A further 45 per cent of men and 33 per cent of women are overweight. As a nation we are less obese than America, Australia, and Eastern Europe, but fatter than the Scandinavians and Japanese. Over the past 20 years there has been a rapid increase in obesity in developing countries. The health risks are high: an increase of 10 kilos results in a 20 per cent increase in the risk of premature death, and a 30 per cent increased risk of contracting diabetes.

These statistics prompted the British Nutrition Foundation (BNF) to commission a report on obesity, published today. It contains the most up-to-date research by a task force made up of the country's leading experts, chaired by John Garrow, formally professor of human nutrition at St Bartholomew's Medical College, London.

The report dispels a number of 'fat myths'. Many of us are aware that the more you eat, and the less energy you expend, the fatter you become. As the report says: 'One of the few statements about obesity that can be made with absolute certainty is that obesity can only occur when energy intake remains higher than energy expenditure, for an extended period of time.'

At the root of the problem is the fact that we have grown increasingly inactive; although we eat about 750 fewer calories a day than 20 years ago, we expend about 800 fewer calories. However, the trouble with fat, as anyone who has tried to diet knows, is that it's difficult to shift. It's not always that easy to tell exactly how much excess fat we are carrying. Many gyms and health centres do offer to measure fat content, but their methods are somewhat inaccurate, and the best (using infra-red scanners) can assess our body fat only to the nearest kilo.

The report suggests using the body mass index (BMI) to check whether an individual is clinically obese. The one drawback is that it doesn't assess the proportions of lean tissue and fat, and may therefore misrepresent athletes' BMI since they have such a high muscle-to-fat-ratio.

BMI is calculated by weight in kilos divided by height in metres squared. A BMI between 20 and 25 is normal, between 25 and 30 is overweight, and above 30 is clinically obese. Recent research indicates that an individual's waist measurement is a good indicator: statistically there is a health risk in a waist size greater than 94cm (34in) in men, and 80cm (32in) in women.

There is evidence to suggest that obesity levels are genetically inherited. Identical twins who are brought up apart tend to weigh a similar amount; adopted children also have similar fat levels to their biological parents, but not to their adoptive ones. The likelihood of inheriting the same position of body fat as your parents – big thighs or a pot belly – is between 18 and 50 per cent. However, a number of other factors, including environment, lifestyle and mental outlook, can interact with a person's genetic propensity to put on weight.

It is a myth that most thin people have a shrew-like metabolic rate and can eat enormous meals. Not all slim people spend their lives in the gym, but they could burn fat by constant fidgeting. Research conducted on the Pima Indians showed that fidgeting ran in the family, and a lack of it was correlated with a predisposition to obesity in later life.

In fact, overweight people have higher metabolic rates than people of normal weight. This is partly because of bigger mass – someone who weighs 40kg too much is lugging around the equivalent of two suitcases – and partly because weight gain is not entirely fat. About a quarter is extra musculature to support the bulk,

and intestinal and liver tissue also increase; all these are more calorie-hungry than fat.

Most adults possess about half a billion mature fat cells. The number that are full of fat at any one time changes both minute by minute, and on a more long-term basis. Brown fat cells were once all the rage; anyone who was Twiggy-thin was presumed to have a lot of brown fat. We now know that these cells (brown adipose tissue, BAT) are largely found in animals where they are involved in regulating heat, and can influence obesity in rats, but the report suggests that they play only a minor role in human physiology.

The deposition of normal, or white fat cells, is influenced by gender and genetics. Women tend to have more fat deposits on their hips and thighs, for example, which are believed to provide some of the energy for breast-feeding. It used to be thought that the number of fat cells laid down in infancy would be the amount you had for life. According to the report, this is untrue. In one study conducted more than 20 years ago, 28 obese women lost 13 (out of a total of 38) kg of fat over 26 weeks. Their fat cells shrank, but only 2 per cent of them disappeared.

Recent research confirms this: once the number of fat cells a person has been born with are full, more are produced, and although in theory these fat cells can be killed, in practice it is rare. The purpose of a fat cell is to store fat, thus if someone has a large number of fat cells (even if some are empty), they will be predisposed to gain weight. This may be one reason why people who have initially lost weight put it back on. Even removing fat cells by drastic surgical measures, such as liposuction, does not help in the long term as immature fat cells can subsequently develop into mature cells to replace them.

The report claims that anti-obesity drugs may help: 'Drugs will be useful to the extent that they make lifestyle changes easier to achieve, provided that they are cost-effective and safe.' According to Professor Peter Kopelman, from St Bartholomew's and the Royal London School of Medicine and Dentistry, Sibutramine can be effective and has, as yet, not proved to be as harmful as other drugs on the market. It acts on the nervous system by preventing hormones – serotonin and noradrenaline – from being taken up the brain, and combats hunger pangs.

Sibutramine can lead to a 10 per cent reduction in body weight in three months. However, drug use is not a miracle cure and Professor Kopelman recommends this strategy only for those with a BMI greater than 30, who have already attempted to alter their lifestyle and diet. The side-effects of Sibutramine include nausea, insomnia, dry mouth, constipation and an increase in blood pressure and heart rate.

The stark truth is that the only way to maintain weight is to eat sensibly and exercise regularly (at least half an hour of brisk walking five times a week); losing a kilo of fat a week means eating 1,000 fewer calories every day. It may be tough, but in the end a healthy lifestyle is the only effective way to keep trim.

© The Independent
May, 1999

10 key facts on obesity

Information from the British Nutrition Foundation (BNF)

1) Obese people are at increased risk of heart disease, hypertension, non-insulin dependent diabetes, gallstones, osteoarthritis of weight-bearing joints, sleep apnoea, reproductive disorders and some cancers. It is important that obesity is given more prominence as a risk factor for disease. Obesity is a reversible condition, and with careful attention to both prevention and treatment it should be possible to tackle this problem in the future.

2) Between 1980 and 1997, obesity increased in England from 6% to 17% in men and from 8% to 20% in women. The number of men and women who are now overweight is 62% and 53% respectively. The pattern throughout the UK is fairly similar, with little regional variation. Body Mass

*By Amanda Wynne,
Nutrition Scientist*

Index (BMI) increases with age in both men and women up to the age of 64 years, then decreases slightly in older age groups. The relationship between BMI and social class varies with gender. In women, BMI tends to be higher in the manual social classes than in the non-manual social classes. In men, the pattern is less clear. Further, an inverse association has been reported between educational attainment and BMI, particularly amongst women. Vegetarians have a lower BMI than omnivores, although this is likely to be due to factors other than the exclusion of meat from the diet.

3) The 'old myth' that obesity occurs as a result of a low metabolic rate is unfounded. One of the few statements about obesity that can be made with absolute certainty is that obesity can only occur when energy intake remains higher than energy expenditure, for an extended period of time. In other words, where there is a chronic displacement of the energy balance equation (energy in minus energy out = change in body energy stores).

4) Environmental changes that have occurred over the last few years, such as a more sedentary lifestyle and the ready availability of energy dense foods, are the most likely underlying factors in the increasing prevalence of obesity. There are studies that have shown small differences in metabolism between obese subjects and their lean counterparts, but these differences are very subtle and are far outweighed by the impact of environmental influences and behavioural factors. A key strategy in tackling the rising prevalence of obesity must be education about the need for positive lifestyle changes. Health professionals should provide advice both for individuals and at a population level.

5) Predisposition to obesity has often been associated with intakes of high-fat foods. There does seem to be an increased liking for high-fat foods in those predisposed to obesity, for example obese people, previously obese people, non-obese people with a high BMI, children of obese parents and restrained eaters. There is no clear relationship, however, between dietary intakes and obesity. Perhaps a more important area to consider in terms of prevention is the development of new strategies to promote an environment that is 'user friendly' in terms of activity. This will require action from government, local authorities and health authorities to provide affordable recreational facilities and safe environments for walking, jogging or cycling

6) There is increasing recognition that obesity is a serious medical condition. Strategies for both prevention and treatment should include a combination of dietary intervention, behavioural therapy and promotion of physical activity. Effective management by a multi-disciplinary team is important, with equal focus on both weight reduction and weight maintenance.

7) There are a wide variety of dietary interventions available for the treatment of obesity, including low calorie diets, very low calorie diets, milk diets and novel diets. Unfortunately, with many diets, long-term follow-up shows that much of the weight lost is regained. For dietetic success, it is important to focus on the patient's individual needs, to set realistic goals, to instigate small achievable changes rather than large changes, and to focus on weight maintenance. Dietary strategies form an important part of the treatment of obesity.

8) A deeper understanding of weight control and problem solving amongst health professionals should be encouraged. In terms of behavioural therapy, flexible long-term strategies that deal with both diet and activity should be promoted. Emotional issues also need to be addressed. 'Body image dissatisfaction', for example, is highly correlated with obesity, particularly amongst women and younger people; ethnicity can also influence body image. Cognitive behavioural treatments are increasingly addressing the reduction of 'body image distress'; this can make a significant contribution to well-being.

9) Another important consideration in terms of treatment is that of physical activity. There are many benefits of exercise, which go far beyond weight control. For example exercise can reduce depression, anxiety and stress; it can enhance mood and self-esteem; and it can improve sleep quality. There is an increasing trend in inactivity in the UK at the present time, especially in children, and this is a problem that needs to be tackled if the trend in obesity is to be reversed. Recommendations for obese people, in terms of activity, are that: the amount of time spent in sedentary activities should be reduced; vigorous activity should be avoided, bouts of longer periods of moderate and sustained exercise would be more beneficial; and more weight-bearing movement should be encouraged.

10) In those who are clinically obese, where methods such as dietary intervention, behavioural therapy and promotion of physical activity have failed to achieve a weight loss of 10% after 3 months of managed care, it may be appropriate to consider an anti-obesity drug. Orlistat, for example, which is a pancreatic lipase inhibitor, has been available in the UK since 1998. Sibutramine, which promotes satiety, is currently licensed for use in Germany, and may become available in the UK later this year. The recent withdrawal of fenfluramine and dexfenfluramine, as a result of safety concerns, underlies the importance of continued monitoring of anti-obesity drugs to ensure there are no adverse effects.

• The Task Force report, *Obesity*, is now available from the BNF price £29.99.

Notes: This is a summary of the findings from the British Nutrition Foundation conference on Obesity, which was held on 27 May 1999, to launch the Obesity Task Force report. Speakers were Professor John Garrow (Chairman of the Task Force), Dr Ann Fehily (HJ Heinz Company Ltd), Professor Andrew Prentice (London School of Hygiene and Tropical Medicine), Professor Jane Wardle (University College London), Dr David Mela (Unilever Research, Vlaardingen), Ms Mary O'Kane (Leeds General Infirmary), Professor Peter Kopelman (St Bartholomew's and the Royal London School of Medicine) and Professor Ken Fox (University of Bristol). Professor Robert Pickard, Director-General of the BNF, chaired the meeting.

• The British Nutrition Foundation provides independent and authoritative scientific information on the relationship between food, nutrition and health. For more information about the British Nutrition Foundation, see their web site: www.nutrition.org.uk or contact them at High Holborn House, 52-54 High Holborn, London, WC1V 6RQ. Tel: 0171 404 6504, Fax: 0171 404 6747, E-mail: british_nutrition@ compuserve.com

© British Nutrition Foundation (BNF)

The ABCs of exercise

Information from BUPA

Why should I exercise?

The benefits of regular exercise are numerous. Exercise can help prevent heart disease, high blood pressure, stroke, diabetes (Type 2), and depression. Regular exercise can help reduce high blood cholesterol, the effects of osteoporosis (thinning of the bones) and arthritis, and the symptoms of pre-menstrual syndrome and menopause. It can improve balance, muscular strength, and help with poor circulation, and can relieve sleeping problems, stress and anxiety. In so many ways, regular exercise can improve your physical and mental health, no matter what your age.

Do I need to see my doctor before I start exercising?

You should see your doctor before starting an exercise programme if you:
- haven't been active for some time,
- are a man over 40 or a woman over 50 years of age,
- suffer any conditions such as heart or lung disease, high blood pressure, diabetes, arthritis or asthma,
- are a smoker,
- are overweight,
- are pregnant,
- are at risk of having an injury,
- are uncertain about any aspect of your health.

How often and for how long should I exercise to become fit?

Begin your exercise programme slowly. If you are active too quickly, you might injure yourself. Try starting with a 10-minute period of light exercise and gradually build from there. When you are ready, it is recommended that you exercise at least three to four times a week. Try to do 20–30 minutes a session. Those 30 minutes don't have to be continuous. We know that three 10-minute sessions of exercise each day are just as good as one 30-minute workout. Remember that occasional vigorous activity is unwise and possibly dangerous if you're 'out of shape'.

How hard should I be exercising?

We used to be told that only vigorous exercise would make us fit. However, that belief has changed and exercise experts now say that moderate activity on most days of the week provides all the health benefits you need from exercise. Of course, if you want to do more vigorous activity for 30–60 minutes, three or more times a week, you will be even fitter. It is your choice – what is important is how frequently and for how long you exercise, not how hard you do it.

What kind of exercise should I do?

As many types of activity are available, pick those you enjoy. Brisk walking, swimming, jogging, dancing, aerobic classes, cycling or hiking are good options. Find out what activities are available in your area by contacting your local library or recreation department.

You might be surprised to hear that normal everyday activities can also help to improve your health. So the next time you are gardening, housecleaning or taking out the rubbish, remember that it all adds up to fitness.

When should I exercise?

It depends on what sort of person you are and your schedule. If you are a morning person, exercise first thing may be the best. Otherwise, if your schedule allows, you might try the afternoon or early evening. Exercise late at night may interfere with falling asleep, so it is a good idea to leave two or three hours between your activity and bedtime. Remember that you can squeeze exercise into other parts of your day – use the stairs instead of taking the lift, walk part of the way to work or do your housework at a faster rate.

What about warming up and cooling down?

Both are important but simple ways to avoid injury. Try warming up (before active exercise – you don't need to warm up before housework) with five to ten minutes of brisk walking or gentle running on the spot, followed by light stretches. After you have finished exercising, do the same until your heart rate has returned to normal and you feel 'cool'.

What should I wear?

Taking up exercise does not mean you have to spend a fortune on sportswear. For walking or jogging, you simply need a good pair of shoes, and comfortable clothing that is suitable to the weather – loose, light clothing in summer and warm, windproof layers in winter. It is a good idea to wear white, reflective clothing especially if you are outside in the evening.

How do I stay motivated?

Sticking to a regular exercise routine can sometimes be a challenge, but

there are some easy ways to keep you on track. Try exercising with a friend – it is harder to skip a day when someone else is expecting you. Inject fun into your programme by taking part in fun walks, runs, swims or rides. Set small fitness goals for yourself and when you reach them reward yourself – perhaps with new trainers or sportswear. Be flexible – if the weather is bad or you are feeling overtired, give yourself a day off. Finally, if you do stray from your regular fitness routine, do not be hard on yourself. Set a new time and begin again.

How do I know if I have exercised too hard?

Forget the 'no pain, no gain' approach. A little soreness is fine after you first start an exercise programme, but pain is not. Stop exercising and obtain help right away if you feel:
- a tight feeling in your chest,
- pain in your chest, arms or jaw (often on the left side),
- severe shortness of breath,
- a rapid throbbing or fluttering of your heart,
- dizzy, faint or nauseous.

What else do I need to know?

Safety is an issue if you are exercising outside, especially late at night. Many activities are safer and more fun if you do them with a friend. And remember to drink plenty of water before, during and after exercise, particularly if the weather is hot and humid.

© Mosby International/ BUPA 1996-99

General exercises

The majority of general exercise can be undertaken at home. If you plan for 3 times a week of about 30 minutes a day whether all at once or split into 3 x 10-minute sessions, you will see an improvemnt in your general physique.

Listed below are a few examples of the type of exercises you may want to consider putting into your routine.

Warm up

Before undertaking any form of fitness exercise it is important to warm up correctly. By stretching the muscles you will not only decrease the possibility of tearing them, but also increase your recovery time. That is the time it takes for you to stop aching. A good warm-up routine also aids the reduction of the lactic acid build-up which forms in the muscles after exercise and is the cause of pulled muscles and aching limbs.

It should also be remembered that it is vital that you complete the same 'warm down' as you did when warming up, as this is the time when you can do most damage to yourself.

Toe raises

Want some impressive-looking calves? Here's how to get them.

Start out standing on the ground flat-footed, toes pointing straight ahead. Balance yourself, and begin raising yourself up as high as you can on your toes. Do this exercise slowly with control. Lower yourself to the starting position, then repeat. One movement up and back down is called a 'rep'. Try to work up to at least 25 reps.

Advancing to later stages

To make it a little tougher as you progress, do them one leg at a time. You can also turn your feet in and out in order to work different parts of your calves. A set of 25 reps with feet pointing forward, then out, then in, would give you a nice workout.

For an even tougher workout, and to really make those calves grow,

place your toes on the edge of a 2x4, a piece of wood , a thick book or on the stairs, and lower the heels as far as possible. Then raise up on your toes, again as high as you can, and repeat. Again, 25 reps is what you'll be shooting for. This will really make the calves burn.

But please, start out slowly. Don't do too many reps at one time in the beginning, or you won't be walking for the next day or two.

Wall squat

Stand straight with your back pressed against a wall. Feet should be about shoulder width. Lower yourself down into a sitting position, still leaning against the wall. Be certain the front of your feet are in front of your knees... if not, move your feet forward. Hold this position for about 30 seconds, then return to the start. Gradually build up to 3 reps

Crunch

This is an exercise that is good for those troublesome abs. Lie on the floor on your back with your feet up on the couch or a chair or something. Your buttocks should be as close to the couch as possible. To ease the strain on your neck, take a towel and fold it lengthwise, then place it behind your head, grasping both ends. The back of your head should lie comfortably on the towel. Lock your elbows against your sides.

Now very slowly raise your head and shoulders off the ground a few inches. Don't pull with the towel. Allow your abs to do the work. And don't lift too high off the ground . . . you'll get a backache. Just a few inches will do. Squeeze your stomach at the top and hold for a second or two, then slowly lower yourself back to the starting position. That's 1 rep. Work your way up to about 25 reps. Remember to do these slowly and squeeze at the top.

Your goal will be 2-3 sets of 25 reps.

Push ups

Lying face down, place your palms on the floor next to your shoulders. Keeping your back straight push yourself up until your elbows are locked. Your eyes should be looking straight ahead. Tighten your muscles and hold for a second or two, then slowly lower yourself down until your body almost touches the floor. Repeat. Each time up and down counts as 1 repetition. Do as many as you can. Build yourself up to 3 sets of 20 to 25 repetitions.

Be sure to do this movement slowly and flex the muscles at the top of the movement. This will help build your arm muscles, back muscles, shoulders and neck.

Triceps dips

A solid workout bench works best with this exercise; a chair will work, but there's too much chance that it may topple over.

With the bench at the back of you, reach back and bend down until you can place your hands on the bench, palms facing back, hands about shoulder width apart. Place your feet in front of you; you'll be leaning on your heels with your toes pointing straight up in the air. Begin to slowly lower your body as far as you can. You'll feel the strain on your triceps. Push yourself back up to the starting position, again, very slowly. That's 1 repetition. Do 3 sets of 10-12 repetitions. If you're ambitious and want to really get those triceps to grow, do 3 sets of 25 reps 3 times a week, with your feet resting on a chair.

Fitness tip

If you are serious about losing weight and getting fit, you need to combine 2 training methods; strength training and aerobics. Aerobics, such as walking, running, cycling, etc., should be done a minimum of 30 minutes a session, 3 times a week. You'll build a healthy heart and circulatory system and lose weight in the process. Strength training, such as weight lifting, body resistant exercises, cables, etc., should be done at least twice a week. You'll firm up and build muscle. Here's the kicker .

Muscle burns fat

Build muscle and you'll keep burning fat but remember that your diet is also important so don't overdo the food intake.

Exercise for teenagers

By Armand Tecco, M.Ed.

Exercise is not only safe and acceptable for teenagers, it is also integral to gaining health benefits that can last a lifetime. Problems that can arise from exercise are more commonly related to environmental stresses such as dehydration and heat-related illnesses.

Exercise benefits

Teenagers who adopt healthy lifestyle habits such as engaging in regular exercise are more likely to be active and physically fit as adults than teens who don't exercise. Exercise promotes self-confidence, a positive self-image and a sense of achievement – advantages that anyone could use during the awkward teen years. In addition to improved psychological well-being, the benefits derived from exercise are the same for teens as they are for adults:

- weight control
- lowered blood pressure
- improved cardiovascular system
- increased energy and stamina
- stronger immune system
- suppleness and flexibility
- stronger, more toned muscles
- stronger bones.

Starting an exercise programme

This age group presents unique challenges when it comes to starting an exercise programme. Self-conscious teens may refuse to do anything that could expose their apparent clumsiness. Once teenagers decide to co-operate, they may become easily discouraged when the exercise doesn't produce immediate results or if they don't feel competent doing the activity. That's why it's important to choose exercises that fit the interests and skill level of the teen.

Many teens enjoy traditional school athletics, such as football, soccer, baseball, track, basketball, hockey, lacrosse and swimming. For those who are intimidated by team sports, non-competitive alternatives like aerobics classes and jogging build endurance without the added pressure of 'playing to win'. Unstructured play should also be encouraged – bicycle riding, in-line skating and hiking are all terrific ways to get your teen active.

Parents can make a big difference in their teen's physical activity by getting involved, either as a spectator or a participant. When a parent exercises regularly, the teenager is more likely to follow suit. It's a classic case of 'Practise what you preach'!

If you need help directing your teen into a suitable exercise regimen, consult with a fitness professional at a health club or with the coach of a sport that your teen is interested in playing.

Exercise guidelines

A healthy level of physical activity requires participation in activities that increase energy expenditure above resting level. Healthy teenagers should be encouraged to exercise on a regular basis.

Endurance and stamina building

- Your teen should perform cardiovascular exercises that place minimal stress on the joints and use the large muscle groups. Aerobic activities such as walking, jogging, in-line skating, swimming and bicycling build endurance and stamina.
- Teenagers should exercise three to five times per week for 20-30 minutes per session.
- Your child should start slowly and gradually build endurance to a comfortable level. The first three to five minutes should serve as a warm-up to give their body the necessary time it needs to get used to the activity.
- Exercise should continue at a comfortable pace that allows your teenager to talk without difficulty and not perspire profusely.
- Your teen should always slow down for the last three to five minutes of exercise to allow the blood to return from the working muscles to the heart and for the body to return to its resting state. This cool down should not be skipped.

Muscular/skeletal fitness

- Body support movements – such as pull-ups, chin-ups, dips, push-ups and modified sit-ups – are highly recommended forms of resistance exercise for teens.
- A weight-training programme, which builds muscles and bones as well as improving shape, must be carefully monitored and should consist of low intensity, high repetition sets.
- Since teenagers are still developing, no more than three days of weight training are recommended. The exercises should be performed on non-consecutive days, such as Monday, Wednesday and Friday.
- Proper training technique for all of the exercise movements is imperative. Ask a qualified fitness instructor to prescribe appropriate resistance/weight-training exercises, as well as explain proper form and technique to your teenager.
- Jerky movements should be avoided when your teen is performing the exercises. Instead, he or she should use slow and controlled movements.
- Teenagers should use a comfortable weight that allows no fewer than 8 to 15 repetitions per set. Under no circumstance should a teenager lift a weight that only produces less than eight repetitions per set. Besides being dangerous, heavy weights can be potentially harmful to developing skeletal and joint structures.

- As progress is made, your teen can increase the number of repetitions and then start increasing the weight of the resistance. The volume and intensity of training should be increased no more than 10 per cent a week.
- Teenagers should perform one or two sets of eight to 10 different exercises (8 to 15 repetitions per set), using all major muscle groups.
- All exercises should go through the full range of motion.

Flexibility, balance and mobility

Flexibility enables us to bend and move easily. It improves co-ordination and posture as well as reducing the risk of injury and stiffness. Stretching exercises help bodies stay supple.

- Teenagers should perform stretches for all of the major muscle groups, such as legs, chest, back and shoulders. These exercises can be done daily or at least three times per week.
- All exercises should be performed in a slow, controlled manner, holding all stretches for 10 to 30 seconds without bouncing.
- Your teenager should do stretches after their regular workout, while their muscles are still warm.
- To further enhance balance and co-ordination, teenagers should participate in group activities that require learning varied skills.

Special precautions

- A paediatrician should first examine teenagers, especially before beginning a weight-training programme. Also see the doctor for pre-season physicals, which are usually required for team sports.
- Avoid heavy weight-training exercises that can place undue strain on a growing teen.
- Parents concerned about the rare incidence of sudden death in children and young athletes should realise that the most common cause is underlying cardiovascular disease and not exercise itself. A complete physical examination can help allay fears.
- Proper hydration is essential. Children and teens tend to acclimate to heat slowly and over-exert themselves quickly. Make sure kids are drinking plenty of fluids. During vigorous activity, fluid intake should occur every 15 to 20 minutes.
- Check for signs of overheating such as a red face, light-headedness, weakness, cramps, nausea, head-ache, and moist, clammy skin. Move the teen to a cool, shaded area to rest and drink water.
- Provide the protective equipment that is recommended for each sport.
- Discourage any teen from partici-pating exclusively in one sport, which can lead to stress fractures and mental burnout. Variety is much better for a growing body.
- Make sure teenagers take part in sports that match their maturity and compete against other teen-agers similar in size and develop-mental age.
- Parents should be on the lookout for anabolic steroids, drugs used by some athletes to build muscle, increase strength and improve performance. Steroids have many deleterious effects, including behavioural changes such as depression and hostility as well as physical changes such as acne, baldness, sterility and liver disease.

Do I really need to warm up?

By Barbara A. Brehm, Ed.D.

Everyone says to warm up for 10 to 15 minutes at the beginning of your workout. But are there times you could safely skip the warm-up and get right to work, especially when you're in a hurry? How important is warming up? What does it accomplish, and how long does it take? Here are some points to consider the next time these ques-tions arise.

Why warm up?

A good warm-up raises your body temperature and gradually increases the demands placed on the cardio-vascular system. By building slowly from low to higher intensity, your body has time to adequately prepare for more vigorous activity.

How important is warming up?

Warming up is always a good idea. When your metabolic rate increases slowly, your energy production systems have time to adjust. Oxygen delivery to the exercising muscles occurs more easily at higher muscle temperatures. A warm-up increases blood flow to the working muscles and improves the ability of the muscles to produce energy aero-bically. This makes exercise feel easier, so you can enjoy your activities more.

A warm-up is especially import-ant for vigorous activity. It helps to

prevent the abnormal heart rhythms that sometimes occur in response to the sudden onset of vigorous exercise. A warm-up allows blood flow to the heart to increase gradually so that by the time a higher heart rate is required, the heart has adequate oxygen and nutrients to do its job.

An athlete wouldn't think of performing without a warm-up, since muscles function better at higher temperatures. They contract and relax more quickly and move more easily. The energy production systems go into high gear, and nerve transmission accelerates, so co-ordination improves as well. Athletes also value the psychological benefits of a good warm-up as they prepare for their upcoming performance.

What's the best way to warm up?

A good warm-up mimics the activity you will be doing, but at a lower intensity that gradually builds to your workout pace. It may also include other types of exercises to raise your metabolic rate and body temperature. Once you are warm, stretching exercises are designed to prevent injury.

To warm up for a brisk walk, simply begin your walk at a comfortable pace and gradually speed up after five or 10 minutes. You may stretch after the warm-up, at the end of your walk or both.

A group exercise leader may present segments of an upcoming routine for about 10 minutes, perform some limbering and stretching exercises, and then pick up the pace. Athletes preparing to play a sport might perform a general warm-up that includes low-intensity aerobic activity, calisthenics and stretching, followed by a specific warm-up with movements that mimic their event.

Is warm-up always necessary?

Aren't there times, such as during low-intensity exercise, when a warm-up is unnecessary? Low-intensity exercise does not pose the challenges to the cardiovascular and musculo-skeletal systems that vigorous exercise does. However, it still makes sense to start off slowly and build gradually, even if you save your stretching for after the activity.

People with cardiovascular risk factors (which includes most adults) should be especially careful to begin activity at a low intensity that takes 10 to 15 minutes to build to a more moderate pace.

Many people have old injuries that require extra care, or certain areas that seem more prone to overuse injuries, such as tendonitis. A little extra attention to these special areas before and after physical activity can provide a bit of physical therapy and prevent future problems.

When is the best time to stretch?

The best time to stretch is when muscles and joints are nice and warm. A few brief stretches after the warm-up may help prevent injury, especially in sensitive areas. A longer period of stretching (10 or more minutes) after your workout, when you are usually the warmest, will help maintain or increase flexibility.

• Barbara A. Brehm, Ed.D., is associate professor of Exercise and Sport Studies at Smith College, Northampton, Mass.

Are your trainers fit to take the pace?

If your sports shoes are worn out, you run the risk of permanent damage. Peta Bee investigates

If there is one item of footwear that bridges all generation gaps, it is the trainer. Between us – young children, arthritic grannies and everyone in between – we buy four million pairs of them every year; the British market exceeds £175 million. Yet, even as our collective enthusiasm for fitness continues to break records, experts are not sure this is money well spent.

Leading podiatrists warn that some trainers are potentially harmful for our feet. Badly made, ill-fitting and worn-out sports shoes, they say, can cause problems ranging from slight aches to acute pain and long-term damage.

Simon Costain, a podiatrist at the Harley Street Gait and Posture Clinic, has treated countless trainer-induced injuries. The most common, he says, are caused by sports shoes with too little support on the upper, which results in feet pronating (rolling inwards) further than they should.

'It is quite natural for most people's feet to pronate slightly when they are running, but some shoes don't compensate for this,' says Costain. 'Wearing trainers that cause over-pronation can result in lower backache, hip pain, runner's knee, shin pain and problems on the arch and ball of the foot.'

The amount of cushioning provided by a running shoe can be another problem. Each time your foot strikes the ground as you run, it absorbs the force of four times your body weight. This reverberates up through the leg and into the spine.

Badly made, ill-fitting and worn-out sports shoes can cause problems ranging from slight aches to acute pain and long-term damage

---

There is little doubt that a spongy shoe helps to absorb much of the shock and prevent related injuries. But, after years of being told that the more cushioning a running shoe offers, the better, it is now thought that too much bounce in the sole is also a risk.

'Shoes with a high degree of cushioning are necessary only for people with high arches – about five per cent of the population,' says Costain. 'For anyone else, too much sponginess means too much unnecessary movement. Your feet can literally wobble out of control.'

A recent *Which?* report found that many sports shoes had design flaws. There were heel tabs that dug into the Achilles tendon, causing it to become inflamed; some shoes bent under the arch of the foot rather than at the ball, weakening support and straining the feet; and 14 of the 18 shoes tested were found to be inflexible and uncomfortable.

Investing a small fortune in your trainers is not the answer. It certainly won't ensure you get a better constructed shoe.

'There are a lot of gimmicks at the more expensive end of the market and, in many cases, manufacturers make unjustified claims,' says Costain. 'My advice would be not to opt for the cheapest shoe around, but to choose a pair in the mid-price range of £60-£80. For your feet's sake, it is better value to buy two pairs of trainers at £60 than one high-fashion pair at £120.'

According to Trevor Prior, a specialist in podiatric surgery and podiatrist to several Premiership football clubs, the overall quality and design of running shoes is improving and there are plenty of well-made trainers on the market.

Very often, consumer ignorance has a part to play in trainer injuries. A common mistake is to buy shoes that are too small. These constrict the toes and increase the risk of bruising on the toenails and heels.

'In general, you will need a half-size bigger in sports shoes than in regular footwear,' says Prior. He advises trying on new trainers in the afternoon, when feet have swollen and, since feet swell further when you exercise, to wear a reasonably thick pair of socks.

'Ideally, your heel should fit snugly in the cup and the fit should be just tight enough not to allow any movement up and down or from side to side when you walk.'

Attached though you might be to the trusty old trainers you have been jogging in for so long, there comes a time when you must put emotions aside and accept that your shoes are probably doing you more harm than good.

'Trainers have a shelf life of six months to one year, depending on how often you use them. You should definitely replace them after running a total of 500 miles,' says Prior. 'If you've had a pair for longer than that, bin them.'

Achieving a balanced diet

Putting the advice into practice

For many people, achieving a balanced diet in practice will mean:

Eating more starchy foods such as bread, potatoes, rice and pasta
These are already popular foods and increased consumption will help reduce the amount of fat and increase the amount of fibre in the diet. Adding fat to these foods should be avoided or kept to a minimum. Changing the balance of foods eaten will help. An example of this is making sandwiches with thicker bread, less filling and less spread, or having more rice or pasta with less sauce.

Eating more fruit and vegetables
It has been suggested that individuals aim for at least five portions a day (excluding potatoes). Most fruit and vegetables are low in fat (unless butter, oil, margarine, or cream have been added), so eating these foods instead of foods higher in fat can help to reduce total fat intake. It will also increase intakes of fibre, vitamins and minerals. Some of the vitamins are antioxidants, e.g. vitamin C and carotenes. Fruit (not covered with cream, sugar or syrup) and vegetables (without added fat or oil) are low in energy so can be useful in slimming diets.

Choosing leaner cuts of meat and lower-fat versions of commonly eaten foods such as dairy products
This will help reduce the amount of fat, particularly saturated fatty acids, in many people's diets. Trimming meat, choosing cooking methods which do not require added fat (e.g. grilling) and eating smaller portions of high-fat foods can all be helpful.

Drinking sensibly
Some people who drink alcohol drink

too much at any one time, thus risking their health. The current guidelines are:

Men
Regular consumption of between 3 and 4 units a day by men of all ages will not carry significant health risk

Consistently drinking 4 or more units a day is not advised as a sensible drinking level because of the progressive health risk it carries.

The health benefit from drinking relates to men aged over 40 and the major part of this can be obtained at levels as low as one unit a day, with the maximum health advantage lying between 1 and 2 units a day.

Women
Regular consumption of between 2 and 3 units a day by women of all ages will not carry any significant health risk

Consistently drinking 3 or more units a day is not advised as a sensible drinking level because of the progressive health risk it carries.

Balance of good health
The 'Balance of Good Health' is a food selection guide produced

jointly by the Health Education Authority, the Department of Health and the Ministry of Agriculture, Fisheries and Food, which is intended to help people understand and enjoy healthy eating. It is based on the Government's Eight Guidelines for a Healthy Diet which include:

- enjoy your food
- eat a variety of different foods
- eat the right amount to be a healthy weight
- eat plenty of fruit and vegetables
- don't eat too many foods that contain a lot of fat
- don't have sugary foods and drinks too often
- if you drink alcohol, drink sensibly.

The 'Balance of Good Health' is in pictorial form and depicts a plate showing the proportion and types of foods needed to make up a balanced diet. It is important to remember that it is not necessary to achieve this balance at each meal but it can apply to the food eaten over a day or even a week. Dishes containing more than one food can also fit into the model. A pizza, for example, has a dough base with a topping. The dough base counts as a starchy food so trying to have a thick base would be good. If the pizza is homemade the topping could be made with reduced-fat cheese or less cheese and more tomato. Including a side salad with the pizza would increase the amount of vegetables eaten and fruit could be eaten to complete the meal.

The guide applies to all people including those who are above the desired weight for height, vegetarians and people of all ethnic origins. It does not apply to children under two years of age and people with special dietary requirements. People under medical supervision should check with their doctor to see if they should use the guide.

- The above information is an extract from the web site of the British Nutrition Foundation (BNF), which can be found at www.nutrition.org.uk/ or see page 42 for postal address details.

© British Nutrition Foundation 1999

The five food groups

Bread, other cereals and potatoes

What's included
Other cereals means things like breakfast cereals, pasta, rice, oats, noodles, maize, millet and cornmeal.

Main nutrients
Carbohydrate (starch), fibre (NSP), some calcium and iron, B vitamins

Recommendations
Eat lots

Fruit and vegetables

What's included
Fresh, frozen and canned fruit and vegetables and dried fruit. A glass of fruit juice can also contribute. Beans and pulses can be eaten as part of this group.

Main nutrients
Vitamin C, carotenes, folates, fibre (NSP) and some carbohydrate

Recommendations
Eat lots

Milk and dairy foods

What's included
Milk, cheese, yoghurt and fromage frais. This group does not include butter, eggs and cream.

Main nutrients
Calcium, zinc, protein, Vitamin B12, B2, Vitamins A and D

Recommendations
Eat or drink moderate amounts and choose lower-fat versions whenever you can.

Meat, fish and alternatives

What's included
Meat, poultry, fish, eggs, nuts, beans and pulses.
Meat includes bacon and salami and meat products such as sausages, beefburgers and paté. These are all relatively high-fat choices. Beans, such as canned baked beans, and pulses are in this group.
Fish includes frozen and canned fish such as sardines and tuna, fish fingers and fish cakes.

Main nutrients
Iron, protein, B vitamins, especially B12, zinc , magnesium

Recommendations
Eat moderate amounts and choose lower-fat versions whenever you can.

Foods containing fat, foods containing sugar

What's included
Foods containing fat: Margarine, butter, other spreading fats and low-fat spreads, cooking oils, oil-based salad dressings, mayonnaise, cream, chocolate, crisps, biscuits, pastries, cake, puddings, ice-cream, rich sauces and gravies. Foods containing sugar: Soft drinks, sweets, jam and sugar as well as foods such as cake, puddings, biscuits, pastries and ice-cream.

Main nutrients
Fat, including some essential fatty acids, but also some vitamins. Some products also contain salt or sugar.

Recommendations
Eat foods containing fat sparingly and look out for the low-fat alternatives.
Foods containing sugar should not be eaten too often, as they can contribute to tooth decay.

© British Nutrition Foundation 1999

Diet and weight

Information from BUPA

Why is a healthy weight important?

Achieving and maintaining a healthy weight is important for overall health. It can reduce the chances of developing serious diseases and conditions like heart disease, stroke, diabetes, high blood pressure, hip and knee damage, and constipation. It can also make you feel well and have more energy. To achieve a healthy weight and to stay that way may take some effort, but by sticking to the basics of a healthy diet, it can be done.

What is a healthy diet?

A healthy diet means eating a wide variety of foods from four main food groups:

- bread, other cereals and potatoes
- fruit and vegetables
- milk and dairy foods
- meat, fish and alternatives.

Bread, other cereals and potatoes

Choices from this food group should form the basis of your daily meals because they contain high levels of fibre and nutrients. Rice, pasta, noodles, lentils, bread and sweet potatoes are just a few of the options. When possible, choose whole-grain varieties as they provide more fibre, fill you up faster and help to keep your bowel movements regular.

Fruit and vegetables

Fruit and vegetables are an important source of dietary fibre and are rich in vitamins. You should try to include at least five servings of fresh, frozen or canned fruits and vegetables in your daily diet. Avoid overcooking as it can destroy many of the vitamins. Choose your fresh produce carefully. Remember that storing it improperly or storing it for too long reduces the vitamin content.

Milk and dairy foods

Dairy foods are a good source of protein and calcium, but they can be

high in saturated fats. You should choose low-fat varieties of milk, yoghurt, cheese and fromage frais.

Meat, fish and alternatives

Meat, fish, poultry, eggs, beans, lentils and offal are some of the choices that provide important protein in your diet. It is a good idea to eat fish (particularly oily fish, like sardines or salmon) at least once a week, since these contain unsaturated fats. When you can, remove the fat from meat and the skin from poultry as this cuts down on the fat content considerably. So does the cooking method you use: rather than frying, try grilling, steaming, microwaving or baking.

Water

Water is vital to life. It is essential for the chemical processes in our cells and for the maintenance of normal bowel function. Try to drink at least eight cups of water each day.

How much fat can I have?

Although you should not eliminate fat completely from your diet, try to limit fat to no more than 30% of your daily calories. Use butter, margarines and oils sparingly – a scrape or a smear is sufficient. Cutting back on calories from fat leaves room to eat healthier foods, like whole-grains, fruits and vegetables – foods you can eat more of for fewer calories.

Some fat is better for you than others. Saturated fats (found in red meat and dairy products) tend to increase the amount of unwanted cholesterol in the body. Unsaturated fats (found in fish and vegetable oils) tend to decrease the amount of unwanted cholesterol in the body. You should therefore try to cut down on foods that contain saturated fats and eat more foods that contain unsaturated fats

Should I avoid sugar?

Like fat, sugar is acceptable in small quantities, but overall it is not a vital part of healthy eating. Lots of foods, particularly prepared foods, already contain quantities of sugar. You may treat yourself with an indulgence (such as cake or biscuits) now and then, but make sure the serving is small.

How important are serving sizes?

Serving sizes are usually included on food labels to give an idea of the calorie and nutrient content. Serving sizes are one of the most important tools for a healthy diet, because they can help you work out if you are eating enough or too much food. Sometimes, however, serving sizes can be confusing and may be smaller than you think. This is particularly true for foods called 'reduced fat' or 'light' which may have smaller serving sizes than their regular counterparts. To make sure you know what is meant by a serving size, check the label carefully.

Can I skip meals to save calories?

Skipping meals may lead to over-eating because you become so hungry that you snack on whatever is closest at hand. Make sure you eat regular meals and only occasional, healthy snacks. A wholesome breakfast should be at the top of a healthy eating list, and it helps you stick to your eating plan throughout the day.

What about eating out?

Although you have less control over the ingredients and preparation, you can make healthy food choices even when eating out. Avoid fried food, especially deep-fried dishes, and ask for salad dressings and sauces on the side so you can control how much you use. Request that your meal be prepared in a low-fat way, such as grilling or baking. Portion sizes at restaurants

are often larger than at home, so remember to leave extra food on your plate or ask that it be wrapped up to take with you.

What about drinking alcohol?

Alcoholic drinks are high in calories and offer no nutrition. If your aim is to lose weight, avoid alcohol for the time being, particularly because it can increase your appetite and decrease your willpower. If you do drink, do so in moderation: two

standard drinks per day for men and one standard drink per day for women is a good guide.

Is exercise important?

Exercise not only helps you lose weight or maintain a healthy weight, it also tones your muscles and helps you look more trim. Regular exercise is also good for your heart, bones and a sense of well-being. Try to be active every day by doing moderate exercise that you enjoy. Good choices include brisk walking, swimming and cycling.

How can I maintain a healthy weight permanently?

Achieving and maintaining a healthy weight requires a lifelong commitment to healthy eating. Learn to enjoy healthier, low-fat foods and realise that fad diets, liquid meals and diet pills are not the answer. Changing your behaviour is the key. Take time to assess your eating, cooking and shopping habits, and work out strategies to improve them for your long-term health and well-being.

Healthy eating – facts and figures

Choosing foods for a healthy diet doesn't mean giving up your favourite foods

Enjoy your food

Eating is an important part of everyone's lives. Food should be enjoyable as well as nutritious – there is no nourishment in food that is uneaten. All foods provide some nutrients and contribute to the taste, smell, colour, texture and enjoyment of the whole meal. Making enough time to relax while eating and to eat with friends or family whenever possible can play an important part in enjoying meals.

Eat a variety of different foods

No single food provides all the nutrients required for the body to remain healthy and work properly. So a mixture of foods needs to be

eaten throughout life. Choosing foods for a healthy diet doesn't mean giving up favourite foods. But variety and a change towards more vegetables, fruit, bread, breakfast cereals, potatoes, rice and pasta is what matters. Snacks as well as meals count towards the balance.

The Balance of Good Health shows the types and proportions of foods needed for a well-balanced and healthy diet. It is based on five food groups which are:

- Fruit and vegetables
- Bread, other cereals and potatoes
- Milk and dairy foods
- Meat, fish and alternatives
- Foods containing fat. Foods containing sugar.

Choosing a variety of foods from the first four groups every day will help ensure that the body gets the wide range of nutrients it needs.

Eat the right amount to be a healthy weight

Food provides the energy which is used up in keeping the body functioning properly. Each person needs a different amount of energy (calories) and therefore each individual differs in the amount of food they should eat. However much people need, the proportions of food from the five groups remain the same. Things that affect people's overall energy needs are:

- Gender (women tend to need less energy than men)

- Age (older adults tend to need less energy than adolescents and young adults)
- Body size (heavy people need more energy than light people, however, being overweight means less energy is needed to achieve a healthy weight)
- Being very physically active (the more active a person, the greater their energy needs).

It's not good for long-term health to be either underweight or overweight. Not eating enough for the body's needs could lead to ill health. Overeating can cause overweight which in turn can lead to ill health, including heart disease, high blood pressure or diabetes. A healthy weight can be achieved and maintained both by being physically active and by not eating more calories than are used up.

Eat plenty of foods rich in starch and fibre

Foods like bread, other cereals and potatoes are rich in starch and can be good sources of fibre. Starch and fibre are names for groups of carbohydrates. There are different sorts of starch and fibre and these are found only in plants or foods made from plants. Most people do not eat enough of the starchy, fibre-rich foods like bread, potatoes, rice and pasta. They are versatile, nutritious and relatively cheap. Whole-grain cereal foods are particularly rich in fibre, which helps to prevent constipation. Fibre in fruit, pulses (beans, lentils and chickpeas) and vegetables can help to reduce the amount of cholesterol in the blood.

Many people still mistakenly believe that starchy foods such as bread and potatoes are particularly fattening, but this is not the case. Starch provides less than half the calories of the same weight of fat. However, adding concentrated sources of calories, such as fat, to starchy foods, for example cooking potatoes in oil or fat, greatly increases their calorie content.

Eat plenty of fruit and vegetables

There is growing evidence that diets rich in fruit and vegetables reduce the likelihood of developing chronic diseases, such as coronary heart disease and possibly some cancers, in later life. Currently many people would benefit from increasing the amount of fruit and vegetables that they eat. A balanced diet contains at least five portions of fruit and vegetables a day.

Don't eat too many foods that contain a lot of fat

Some fat is needed in the diet. Certain fats are essential to health, some contain vitamins and they help to make foods pleasant to eat. However, many people eat far more fat than they need, and a diet high in fat in addition to other factors, including smoking and lack of exercise, can increase the risk of heart disease. It is easy to spot some fat, like the fat on the outside of meat, fat spreads and so on. But there is a lot of fat which cannot be seen, in pastry, most types of pies, cakes, biscuits, chocolate, and some meat products like sausages and burgers and their vegetarian alternatives. Most labels show the fat content of food, and there are many lower-fat versions of foods available in the shops.

Don't have sugary foods and drinks too often

Eating sugary foods frequently is the main cause of tooth decay. Bacteria on the teeth (in plaque) use sugar to make acid and this causes decay. Regular brushing helps to remove plaque.

Because sugars contain calories and no other nutrients it is sensible for people who are overweight to cut down on their intake of sugar and sugary foods and drinks.

Ideas for healthy snacks include fresh fruit; raw chopped vegetables such as carrot and celery sticks; low-fat yoghurts; plain popcorn; bread-sticks; currant buns, scones or teabreads.

Good catering practice
- Unsaturated fats used in preference to saturated fats.
- Skimmed and semi-skimmed milk used in cooking instead of full-fat milk.
- Vegetables cooked using the minimum amount of water to prevent vitamin loss.
- Salt use minimised – use herbs and spices to flavour dishes.
- Use at least a quarter wholemeal flour to make pastry.
- Make pies with a top crust only.
- Bread for sandwiches cut thickly.
- If potatoes are offered, provide an alternative to fried potatoes.
- Milk and dairy products should be reduced-fat types.
- Meat and poultry should be as lean as possible or trimmed of fat.
- Meat dishes should be extended with pulses or vegetables where possible.
- Milk, fruit juice or tap water offered as alternatives to canned drinks.

© Wired for Health, Crown Copyright

Obesity versus overweight

Know the difference

By Dr Diane Wakat Ph.D.

Have you heard any of these exasperated comments? 'My doctor says I am overweight, and I need to lose about 15 pounds.' 'Look at how obese these clothes make me look!' In our attempts to describe our body composition, particularly using the scale as a universally available measurement device, we use several words synonymously: overweight and obese. But they are not synonyms, and their careless use actually does us a disservice.

The term 'obese' or 'obesity' should actually be reserved for a very specific situation, and that is to describe people who are at definite clinical risk because of the excess amount of body fat that they have. For men, this is considered to occur when their body fat exceeds 20% of their total weight. For women, they are defined as obese – and at clinical risk – when their body fat exceeds 30% of their total weight.

Otherwise, they are not obese, although they may be either 'overfat' or 'overweight'. 'Overfat' indicates an amount of body fat that is above desirable, can certainly affect personal appearance and how clothes fit, but does not put the person at clinical or medical risk. 'Overweight' is exactly that: overweight. This term simply indicates that the person weighs more than some generally acceptable standard says he or she should. An example of such a standard is the Metropolitan Height-Weight charts. For adult men and women, there is a weight range that is considered healthy – based upon the insurance companies experiences with thousands of people.

Unfortunately, the height-weight charts do not provide as sophisticated a method of determining clinical risk as we need. For instance, many men and women now engage in regular physical exercise – including resistance exercise, i.e., weight training. For many of these people, the addition of a healthy, metabolically active amount of muscle actually makes it appear on the height-weight charts as if they weigh too much. They may now be 'overweight' but they are certainly not 'overfat'. Nor is the scale a good measurement device. They do weigh more, even though they may wear a smaller clothing size.

> *To think that you're too fat, when you're not, can severely influence how you feel about yourself. Self-esteem can plummet, even if the information is false*

Why do we need to tighten up our vocabulary on this subject of how much we weigh and how much fat we have? Many reasons. One is the importance of providing accurate clinical information to people. They need to know the truth about their health status. Another very important reason is psychological, for both men and women. To think that you're too fat, when you're not, can severely influence how you feel about yourself. Self-esteem can plummet, even if the information is false.

A third reason deals with insurance. To have an insurance company treat 'overweight' as overfat can have serious consequences on the cost and even the availability of health or life insurance coverage. It's not fair, even though it's still the industry standard to use height-weight charts to determine coverage.

The fourth reason is also very important. If we don't know whether the person is 'overweight', 'overfat' or 'obese', it limits our ability to provide the proper guidance and advice for health behaviour strategies. So be careful with how you describe yourself. If you're overweight, fine. If you're overfat, make some changes in your diet and exercise plans. But don't mistake being overweight for being at increased risk.

• Dr Diane Wakat Ph.D. is the Director of The Nutrition Clinic and President of Intelligent Nutrition Systems.
The above information is an extract from the Intelligent Nutrition Systems web site which can be found at www.nutrition4you.com
© 1997-1999, Intelligent Nutrition Systems, Inc.

Aerobic exercise

Exercise, fitness and leisure

The early 1980s saw aerobic exercise become one of the most in-demand exercise routines. Based on a low-impact but sustainable and constant movement, it involved a steady constant motion of the muscles and the increasing of the body's demand for oxygen. In this manner aerobic exercise works the heart muscle making it bigger and stronger. Examples of aerobic exercises are walking, running, swimming, cycling and the now familiar aerobic classes. The introduction of the STEP enhanced the level of exercise during the time of the work-out but early problems were discovered with badly designed steps that caused bone and muscle pain. New steps are now designed specifically for low-impact work-out. While you want the exercise to be intensive you don't want to overdo it. The heart is the key to aerobic exercise and you should take it easy in building up to your optimum level. As a guide your target heart range (THR) is 60-75% of 220 minus your age. During exercise take your heart beat frequently and increase your exercise to reach your target heart range, but if you start to exceed it, slow down. Exercising for 20-30 minutes three times a week will help you become fitter.

Make fitness a priority

90 minutes a week of exercise split over 3 sessions is ample for getting your body into a much fitter state. Now 90 minutes doesn't sound a long time but the biggest problem with increasing your fitness is one of willpower, a bit like stopping smoking. There always seems to be something else you could be getting on with.

The first thing to do to overcome this is to plan it out. Look at what you like doing or at the very least what you are prepared to do if it came to it. The list below can be a starting point.

- Walk on your lunch hour or coffee break.
- Change social activities from getting a drink to getting together for a softball game, bicycle ride, or a walk.
- Do a business exercise session rather than a business lunch.
- Pedal your way to fitness and enjoy the scenery and the company of family or friends.
- If you work from home, don't get out of bed and go straight downstairs and start working. Walk or jog for 10 minutes first. This way you will soon feel you are actually 'going to work' and therefore have done something before getting there.

Work aerobic exercise into a daily routine

To increase your physical activity doesn't always mean going to the gym. Try putting it into your daily routine. If you do this, you are more likely to keep doing it because you don't have to go out of your way to exercise. Some tips to improve your physical activity:

- Deliberately park your car in the furthest parking space away or if you catch the bus, walk to the next stop.
- Take stairs whenever possible – particularly if you are going four floors or less. Even if you work on the 60th floor, try climbing a few flights and then taking the elevator just shy of your floor and walk the rest of the way.
- Hand deliver messages rather than using the phone, fax or e-mail.
- Wash your own car on good days instead of using the car wash.
- Take your dog for a walk more than once a day.
- Don't use the remote control, get up and change the TV channel.
- Stop smoking.
- Eat healthier.

A fun way of encouragement is for you and your co-workers to have contests on the most creative ways of sneaking activity into your daily routine.

- The above is an extract from Exercise & Fitness on the Web which can be found at www.exercise.co.uk/

© www.exercise.co.uk/

SHALL WE EXTEND THIS BUSINESS MEETING ANOTHER COUPLE OF MILES?

ALL IN FAVOUR – KEEP PEDALLING!

Does exercise affect our mood?

By Armand Tecco, M.Ed.

You may have heard of the natural high experienced by people who exercise regularly. Marathon runners, elite cyclists and other highly active individuals describe a feeling of exhilaration when engaged in their favourite activity and for a brief period after they finish. Quite simply, it feels good to give your body a vigorous workout.

What is the reason for this? One of several theories holds that aerobic exercise releases mood-altering substances called endorphins from the pituitary gland. Endorphins, which are compounds found in the body, improve our mood and relieve pain. They also reduce the levels of cortisol in the bloodstream. Cortisol is a hormone linked to stress and depression.

In a recent study, the level of lactic acid in the blood was found to be one of the measures most associated with endorphins, suggesting that strenuous effort that produces lactic acid is more likely to lead to the release of endorphins.

Although researchers have not proven a direct cause-and-effect relationship between exercise and a better mood, it is widely believed that by improving the fitness levels of our heart and lungs through regular physical activity we can improve our mood. Furthermore, exercise boosts our self-esteem and self-confidence by giving us a sense of accomplishment and independence.

Preliminary results from a major study on depression conducted at Duke University show that intense physical activity – rather than sustained regular exercise – may be the most effective way to reduce feelings of depression, anger and fatigue. The study is part of a larger, five-year study comparing these three treatments for depression: a four-month exercise programme, drug therapy and a combination of exercise and medication.

In the study, 55 participants over the age of 50 completed a lengthy Profile of Mood Survey to assess their current mood. Then they walked on a treadmill for up to 15 minutes at a maximum, exhaustive effort. After exercising, they completed the survey again. Participants experienced an 82 per cent reduction in feelings of depression, tension, fatigue, anger or confusion.

Throughout this century, more than 100 studies have examined the relationship between exercise and depression. D.M. Landers reviewed this literature in an article titled 'The Influence of Exercise on Mental Health', which appeared in the December 1997 edition of *The President's Council on Physical Fitness* and *Sports Research Digest*. The findings suggest that exercise more effectively relieves depression when the training lasts longer than nine weeks and when it involves more frequent sessions of greater-than-average intensity and duration. The research also shows that exercise decreases depression more than relaxation training or casual recreation. Its effect on depression is roughly similar to that of psychotherapy.

Signs of depression include the following:

- loss of interest or pleasure in job, family, hobbies or sex
- difficulty concentrating or remembering
- physical pains that are hard to pin down
- sleep disturbances
- appetite loss or overeating
- unusual irritability
- loss of self-esteem or an attitude of indifference
- a downhearted period that gets worse or will not go away
- frequent or unexplainable bouts of crying
- recurrent thoughts of death or suicide.

If you are depressed, consult with your physician or a mental health provider who can discuss the various treatments with you in more depth.

• This information is not intended to be a substitute for professional medical advice. You should not use this information to diagnose or treat a health problem or disease without consulting with a qualified health-care provider. Please consult your healthcare provider with any questions or concerns you may have regarding your condition.

© 1998-1999 drkoop.com, Inc.

What is cross-training, and why should I do it?

By Denise Howard

Mary recently started a programme to get in shape. It's a lot of effort for her just managing to stick with a brisk walk on her treadmill 3-5 days a week. Only this week she finally reached her first goal, of being able to do it for 20 minutes continuously without feeling wiped out. She doesn't enjoy the treadmill and doesn't like sweating or the physical feeling of exertion. She's thinking that accomplishment may not be enough motivation to continue; there are too many other things she'd rather being doing.

John found his way past that point long ago and has been a regular exerciser for over a year. But his chosen activity, weightlifting, is starting to feel stale and boring – it's always so predictable, so mindless, and his progress has tapered off. He's been increasingly feeling twinges in his shoulder when he performs push-ups, which he does a lot. And although he thought he was in pretty good shape, a pick-up game of soccer with the kids wiped him out and left him hurting in muscles he didn't know he had.

There's a great solution for both of these exercisers: cross-training! Cross-training is performing a variety of activities, challenging your muscles and your heart in different ways as part of your regular activity schedule. The advantages of cross-training are many; here are a few:
- Develops all-around fitness
- Promotes balanced muscle development
- Prevents 'burnout'
- Prevents overuse injuries.

We've all heard the saying 'Variety is the spice of life.' This turns out to be true for our bodies as well as our minds. By tossing in another activity, you keep your body 'guessing' and your mind engaged.

Mary and John above are both

feeling a little 'burned out' for lack of variety and interest. John is developing an overuse injury in his shoulder, possibly due to an imbalance in muscle development. John has also learned the hard way that his fitness demands aren't being fully met by his weightlifting-only workouts – he's lacking in aerobic capacity and there are many muscles that his weight machines haven't trained. There's nothing inherently wrong with either Mary's or John's current programmes, it's just that adding complementary activities would give them both a physical and mental boost.

Here are just a few examples of how you might incorporate cross-training into your schedule:

If your primary activity is:

Running	try: Swimming
Swimming	try: Bicycling
Step aerobics	try: Cardio-kickboxing
Soccer	try: Rowing
Weightlifting	try: Hiking
Bicycling	try: Weightlifting

In each example, you will either use different muscles, or use the same muscles in a different kind of movement, or both.

Using the same muscles in the same way at the same pace all the time will make them very good at

doing that one thing at that one pace – this is known as the principle of 'specificity of training'. Your body becomes more efficient at performing that activity, meaning it becomes easier both in terms of the work required and the amount of attention you have to focus on your movements. (Think of how effortless world-class ice skaters make their activity look!) But that ease may not translate well to other activities which involve different muscles, or a different kind of movement. Cross-training can ensure you're at least somewhat prepared for anything that comes up!

So, mix up your schedule across the week with two or more complementary activities you think you might enjoy. If one of them loses your interest or turns out to be unsuitable, try a different activity! Exercise doesn't have to be work – it's just a matter of finding the right activities for you. Cross-training is the way to go!

• The above information is an extract from the World Fitness web site which can be found at www.worldfitness.org/

© 1999 World Fitness

Exercise and the heart

Being physically fit enhances the quality and the length of our lives, not just physically but mentally, creating the 'feel-good factor'.

With as little as 20 minutes of exercising 3 times a week you can become more physically fit and if you combine this with incorporating extra activity into your daily routine such as walking more, eating better and not reaching for the remote control of the television you will advance rapidly towards a far healthier lifestyle.

Remember that it is a good idea to see your doctor before starting any exercise programme, particularly if you have any medical condition, have a family history of heart disease, or you are a smoker.

The heart

Fitness is a combination of body composition, muscular performance and cardiovascular fitness with the latter being one of the most important components. Improving your cardiovascular increases the supply of oxygen and energy to your body. It also decreases the risk of heart disease, strokes, high blood pressure and other life-threatening diseases.

Cardiovascular fitness can lead to prolonged endurance and will help you perform to the best of your ability.

When a heart is well conditioned, it is like any other muscle – it becomes stronger and more efficient. A normal heart beats at approximately 70 beats per minute at rest, but a conditioned heart can beat as few as 40 beats per minute. As you can see a healthy heart has to work half as much so as to get the same amount of oxygen to the body.

Aerobic

Aerobic (meaning with oxygen) exercise which involves steady constant motion of the muscles increases the body's demand for oxygen. In this manner aerobic exercise works your heart muscle making it bigger and stronger. Examples of aerobic exercises are walking, running, swimming, and cycling. While you want the exercise to be intensive you don't want to overdo it. The best way to monitor the amount of work you are doing is to measure your heart beat. A target heart range (THR) for you is 60-75% of 220 minus your age. When exercising take your heart beat frequently and increase your exercise to reach your target heart range, but if you start to exceed it, slow down. At the beginning aim for the low end of your target heart range and, as you become fitter, gradually work into the higher range. Exercising for 20-30 minutes three times a week will help you become fitter.

Make fitness a priority

Physical exercise should be given the same level of priority as any important event. Regardless of what exercise you choose, 20-30 minutes 3 times a week should be religiously placed into your schedule. Tips to fit exercise into your schedule are:

- Walk on your lunch hour or coffee break.
- Change social activities from getting a drink to getting together for a softball game, bicycle ride, or a walk.
- Do a business exercise session rather than a business lunch.
- Pedal your way to fitness and enjoy the scenery and the company of family or friends.

Sneak exercise into your daily routine

Increasing your physical activity doesn't always mean having to go to the gym. Try putting it into your daily routine. If you do this, you are more likely to keep doing it because you don't have to go out of your way to exercise. Here are some tips to improve your physical activity:

- Park your car at the far end of the car park and walk. We battle for the closest parking places, but in reality those who get the furthest away are getting the biggest prize.
- When shopping, try entering the shops away from the place you wish to visit or make a habit of walking around all the shops before you begin shopping (it's a good way to check out the sales).
- Take stairs whenever possible – particularly if you are going four floors or less. Even if you work on the 60th floor, try climbing a few flights and then taking the elevator just shy of your floor and walk the rest of the way.
- Hand deliver messages rather than using the phone, fax or e-mail.
- Wash your own car on good days instead of using the car wash.
- Take your dog for a walk more than once a day
- Don't use the remote control, get up and change the TV channel.

A fun way of encouragement

- HEAR THAT?!

- MY HEART IS HAVING THE TIME OF ITS LIFE!!

for you and your co-workers is to have contests on finding the most creative way of sneaking activity into your daily routines.

Heart facts and trivia

The existence of the heart was well known to the Greeks, who gave it the name *Kardia*, still surviving in modern words such as cardiac and tachycardia. Aristotle believed that the heart was the seat of the soul and the centre of man. Romans modified *Kardia* to *Cor*, the latter word still surviving in 'cordial greetings'. The old Teutonic word *herton* was also derived from *Cor* and gives us heart via the medieval *heorte*.

Where is it located?

The heart is situated almost dead centre in the middle of the chest. However, the apex or tip of the heart is shifted towards the left chest wall and hits against the ribs during contraction. Consequently, the rhythm is best detected on the left side, just below the pectoralis.

How big is it?

This depends. Are you a human? Well, then it is generally about the size of your fist. This is not really very big when you think about the job it does. In some animals, such as horses, the heart size to body size ratio is much greater. This helps explain why horses are such great endurance athletes! The heart is also bigger in champion endurance athletes, due to genetics and training.

In a sense, the heart is really two hearts, the left heart and the right. Both sides pump the same amount of blood, but to different locations at different pressures. The right side (right ventricle) pumps oxygen-depleted blood that has returned from the body to the lungs for reoxygenation. This is a short trip and requires little pressure development,

The left side (left ventricle) is the real workhorse, pumping oxygenated blood that has returned from the lungs (the right and left side of the heart are thus connected) to the entire body. That means moving blood through an incredible maze of blood vessels from the top of the head to the toes! Consequently it must develop more pressure each beat (about 120mmHg at rest). The left heart muscle is thicker as a result.

Will training make my maximum heart rate increase?

No, the maximum heart rate is not increased by training! (As we get older, our maximum heart rate decreases.) The major difference in the endurance trained heart is a bigger stroke volume. The trained heart gets bigger and pumps more blood each beat.

Fun and fitness

Get fit, stay fit and enjoy it

Training tips

Warm up and cool down! Always warm up. A slow build-up of the heart rate will gradually increase the oxygen flow to the muscles and prepare the body for vigorous exercise (physically and mentally).

Stretching muscles will prevent injury during the workout and relax them after the workout.

Warm up
- Mobilisation of joints
- Gentle aerobic warm-up
- Major muscle stretches

Cool down
- Aerobic warm-down
- Major muscle stretches
- Mobilisation of joints

Never!
- Never perform exercises that involve hyper-extension of joints – especially where the spine is involved.
- Never 'lock out' joints. This takes joints into hyper-extension and is to be avoided at all costs.

- Never hold your breath during exercise – muscles require oxygen to function, especially during high-intensity aerobic activity.

Always!
- Ensure correct technique. Injuries will only occur when exercise technique is bad.
- Ensure the exercise you are performing is safe. If you are unsure about an exercise, consult your fitness/gym instructor.

- Try to work within your personal 'Heart Rate Training Range'. Working in a range between 75% and 85% of your maximum heart rate is generally ideal for improving aerobic fitness. For specific needs, e.g. fat loss, a more specialised programme can be advised.
- Keep moving. The heart rate should stay in the 'training range' for aerobic capacity to improve and suddenly stopping could cause dizzyness or even fainting.

Note! A high resting heart rate or high blood pressure could result in overstressing the heart during exercise. Low blood pressure could result in dizzyness or fainting.

Warming up
Warming up should consist of:

Mobilisation of joints
Shoulders, elbows, knees, hips, spine, ankles – all major joints should be mobilised so that they are adequately lubricated.

Gentle aerobic warm-up
Approximately five minutes of low-intensity aerobic activity which uses the same muscle groups and similar movements that will be used during the main workout.

Major muscle stretches
Static stretches for each major muscle group, especially those about to be worked.

Reasons for warming up:
Progressive increase in heart rate
This will improve coronary blood flow and help prepare the heart and lungs for the extra demands placed on them as exercise intensity increases.

Gradual increase in oxygen flow to muscles
Muscles require oxygen to function during prolonged physical activity. Warming up ensures that muscles are provided with the gradual increase in oxygen required as exercise intensity increases.

Help prevent early fatigue
If oxygen flow to the muscles is inadequate, the body has to find other means of providing the muscles with energy. Muscular activity will quickly become anaerobic and waste substances such as lactic acid will accumulate. This results in the power output of muscles being reduced and further prolonged activity will therefore be difficult.

Increase muscle temperature
When muscles are tight and cold, increased force is spread to the tendons and other connective tissue. Warming up will lead to greater elasticity of the muscles and flexibility of connective tissue which in turn will help to prevent injury.

Summary!
By warming up, demands are made gradually and progressively on the circulatory and respiratory systems – there is no 'system shock'.

Intensity should gradually increase but not cause undue fatigue.

Warming and stretching the muscles helps prevent injury and will improve overall performance.

Anaerobic fitness
What is anaerobic fitness?
Anaerobic exercise usually refers to activities which require large bursts of energy over shorter periods of time.

During anaerobic exercise, stored 'fuels' such as glycogen provide energy at a fast rate without the need for oxygen.

A person's anaerobic capacity is determined by the size of available 'fuel stores' and the effect that waste products resultant from the 'energy making' process have on muscular activity.

Effects of anaerobic exercise:
As exercise intensity increases towards an individual's maximum aerobic capacity, energy demands can no longer be met by the aerobic system and the body must find other ways of 'making energy'.

Anaerobic Glycolysis is an 'energy making' process but waste products from this process such as lactic acid will quickly reduce the power output of muscles.

A trained individual will have a greater capacity to withstand the build up of waste substances such as lactic acid and increased ability to remove them from the body.

Why exercise anaerobically?
Exercise should be aerobically based but it is inevitable that an individual will have to work anaerobically at some point. By improving anaerobic fitness, an individual will have a greater ability to withstand the onset of fatigue.

The anaerobic system will usually come into play within the first 30 seconds of high-intensity exercise (such as shuttle running).

As fatigue sets in, exercise intensity will decrease and the aerobic system takes over until aerobic capacity is reached. The anaerobic system then takes over again until fatigue makes further exercise very difficult. The body then requires rest in order to 'refuel'.

Aerobic fitness
What is aerobic fitness?
Aerobic fitness means the ability to continue physical activity at less than maximum intensity and withstand the onset of fatigue.

During aerobic exercise, stored carbohydrates and fats are broken down in the presence of oxygen to supply the muscles with energy.

A person's aerobic capacity is determined by their ability to 'take in and use oxygen'.

Longer-term effects of aerobic exercise:
There will be an increase in the surface area of the lungs allowing more oxygen to diffuse into the blood (and waste products to diffuse out).

There will be an increase in the capacity of the blood to carry oxygen which is then delivered to the working muscles.

The working capacity of the heart increases (greater amount of blood pumped out per beat) which should be reflected by a lower heart rate (pulse).

If an individual can take in and utilise oxygen effectively, there will generally be less stress on the heart. The cardio-respiratory system will have an increased ability to deliver and 'feed' the working muscles with the oxygen they require.

Points to remember
To work aerobically, especially if an individual is not a regular exerciser, intensity should not be increased too quickly. If intensity is increased too quickly, aerobic work will become anaerobic, waste substances begin to build up in the muscles and this will rapidly lead to muscular fatigue.

As aerobic fitness increases, an individual can exercise at a higher intensity without beginning to work anaerobically. This means that energy demands are being met by the aerobic system.

Target heart rate

What is the heart rate training range?

It is the predicted optimum heart rate an individual should reach and maintain during exercise in order to improve and maximise the efficiency of the heart and lungs.

Exercising in the correct training range will burn calories and improve cardiovascular fitness.

The training range is a general guide to the recommended intensity of exercise best suited to an individual.

What is the correct heart rate training range?

The heart rate training range for any one individual will be dependent on many factors such as age, current level of fitness and goals that are to be achieved through exercise.

As an individual's aerobic fitness increases, the intensity of exercise will have to increase to keep the heart rate within the target range.

A greater proportion of energy comes from fat when working at lower intensities so an individual wishing to reduce fat would normally work in a lower training range.

For a generally harder workout to improve cardiovascular fitness and to burn more calories overall, a higher training range would be necessary.

The heart rate should be monitored at frequent intervals during exercise. This helps indicate whether aerobic fitness is increasing (heart rate will be lower at the same exercise intensity) or whether the heart is perhaps being worked too hard for a particular individual.

Points to remember:

To work aerobically, especially if an individual is not a regular exerciser, intensity should not be increased too quickly. If intensity is increased too quickly, aerobic work will become anaerobic, waste substances begin to build up in the muscles and this will rapidly lead to muscular fatigue.

As aerobic fitness increases, an individual can exercise at a higher intensity without beginning to work anaerobically. This means that energy demands are being met by the aerobic system.

General rule:

Find your maximum heart rate: 220 minus your age

This heart rate is a maximum rate, preferably not reached – definitely not exceeded.

Find your training range:

75% x maximum heart rate
85% x maximum heart rate

An individual should attempt to remain within this training range for maximum benefit.

If you are unsure what may be your ideal training range, consult your fitness instructor.

Flexibility

What is flexibility?

- Flexibility refers to the capability of an individual to use the muscles and the related joints throughout the full potential range of movement.
- Flexibility/stretching exercises involve lengthening the muscles and aim to extend the range of movement of a joint.

Why is flexibility important?

- Flexibility is probably the most neglected component of physical fitness.
- A lack of flexibility may well affect exercise technique which in turn is likely to reduce the performance potential of an individual.
- Poor flexibility contributes to the many strain and tear injuries that often occur.

How is flexibility maintained and developed?

- Reducing muscle tension to make the body feel more relaxed.
- Increasing the range of movement of joints and muscles

allowing the body to work more efficiently.
- Preventing muscle soreness or muscle tears.
- Improving exercise technique.

When to stretch?

Stretching should always be used in the warm-up and cool-down components of an exercise session.

During the warm-up component:
Stretching should only take place once the muscles are fully warmed up.

During the cool-down component:
Stretching should be combined with the remobilisation of joints after the main exercise has been completed. This is also the ideal time to spend developing and improving flexibility as the muscles will be thoroughly warm as a result of the workout.

Surviving classes

Fitness classes should attempt to improve:
- Aerobic fitness
- Muscle tone and definition
- Muscular strength and endurance
- Flexibility

Ten top tips to help you get the most from your class:

- Always inform your instructor if you have any injuries or other medical conditions. Exercises which may be more appropriate can then be prescribed.
- Ask questions! If you are unsure about any aspect of the class, how exercises can be adapted to better suit you or what an exercise is supposed to be doing – ask!
- Use high-impact or low-impact variations that best suit you. Just because someone else is performing high-impact moves, it does not mean it is necessarily best for you.
- Ensure each and every exercise is performed correctly and in a smooth, controlled manner. Not only will this prevent injury but it will maximise the benefits from performing the exercise.
- If you are finding co-ordination of moves difficult, leave out arm actions and add these when you feel more confident. The main

workout comes from the large leg movements used throughout the session.

- When high-impact moves are used, ensure the knees are kept soft and that heels are brought down onto the floor. This is very important, especially if a sprung floor is not being used.
- Make sure that you drink plenty of fluid, especially in hot weather.
- Wear suitable training shoes. A good pair of training shoes will help prevent unnecessary stress on knee and ankle joints.
- If you begin to feel very fatigued, perform smaller movements, perform an easier version of the exercise or jog/walk around and join in again once you feel ready. It is important that you keep moving, even if it is slowly, as suddenly stopping could cause dizzyness or even fainting.
- Try and concentrate on the muscles working rather than just 'going through the motions' as you work out. 'Feeling' specific muscles working is an indication that the exercise is being performed correctly. Always enjoy your exercise sessions!

Pain-free bike riding

Easy rider!

Breezing around on a bike can make you feel like a kid again. But a stiff back or sore joints can snap you back to reality within minutes – or really hammer you the next day. To keep bike riding pain-free, follow these tips to prevent . . .

An achy back

Adjust the seat and handlebars so that your back's not too stretched out. Your elbows should be slightly bent and your back at no less than a 50-degree angle to the road. Another tip: alternate rounding and arching your back every 10 to 15 minutes. Muscles fatigue quickly and become sore when they have to maintain the same position for a long time.

Knee pain

A seat that's too high or too low can stress your knees. To get the right height, adjust the seat so that there is a slight bend at the knee even when your foot is at its lowest point. More tips: stick to low gears so you spin easily instead of straining in a higher gear, and keep your knees pointing straight ahead as you pedal.

A sore bottom

A large, cushy seat may not be the answer. Too-soft foam may allow you to sink into the hard frame. A seat that's too wide can cause your legs to rub, resulting in chafing. Try seats specially designed for women; they offer extra padding where you need it most. Or, try a gel seat cover.

Another tip

Invest in a good pair of bike shorts. They come with a built-in cushion that pads and protects your bottom. There are also new baggy styles available, as well as underwear versions to wear with regular shorts. (These are all designed to replace regular underpants.)

A stiff neck

When your upper body is too extended, it can cause neck strain. Unless you're a hard-core rider, you can try switching to handlebars that allow you to sit more upright, such as mountain-bike style or the old-fashioned, antler-shaped type. If you really want the aerodynamics of a road bike, make sure you move your neck around frequently, so it's not in one position for too long.

Tingling hands

Gripping the handlebars too tightly for too long can lead to pain, numbness, or tingling. Change hand positions often, and keep your elbows unlocked.

Quick tip

If you're riding for several hours, the best way to avoid all-over aches and pains is to take frequent breaks. When you stop, walk around and do some stretches.

The Internet has been likened to shopping in a supermarket without aisles. The press of a button on a Web browser can bring up thousands of sites but working your way through them to find what you want can involve long and frustrating on-line searches.

And unfortunately many sites contain inaccurate, misleading or heavily biased information. Our researchers have therefore undertaken an extensive analysis to bring you a selection of quality Web site addresses.

* * * * *

Active for Life (Health Education Authority)
www.active.org.uk
Active for Life is a Health Education Authority site designed to help its users think a little bit more about their current physical activity patterns.

Bodies in Motion . . . Minds at Rest
http://library.advanced.org/12153
A web site designed to improve your health, both physically and mentally. Learn what you can do to get in good shape and stay that way. Learn how to deal with the issues that affect you.

Bodyisland
www.bodyisland.com
A lively site which looks at issues including fitness, health, weight loss and nutrition.

British Nutrition Foundation (BNF)
www.nutrition.org.uk
The Foundation promotes the nutritional well-being of society through the impartial interpretation and effective dissemination of scientifically based nutritional knowledge and advice. An informative site.

Cyber Cyclery
http://cyclery.com
Thousands of bicycle enthusiasts around the world use Cyber Cyclery every day to find a wide variety of biking related information, resources and services.

CyberDiet
www.CyberDiet.com
An impressive site with sections on just about everything to do with fitness.

drkoop.com
www.exercise.co.uk
The goal of drkoop.com is to provide accurate, reliable information and the tools needed to contribute to and enable a well-informed public. US-based information but full of resources.

European Food Information Council (EUFIC)
www.eufic.org
EUFIC is an independent, non-profit organisation which provides science-based information on food and food-related topics to the media, health and nutrition professionals, educators, and opinion leaders. Their Food Today articles under the Nutrition and Health link provide useful information.

International Association for the Study of Obesity (IASO)
www.iaso.org
The International Association for the Study of Obesity represents scientists, medical and health professionals throughout the world. It aims to help advance our understanding of the relationship between body weight and health through research and dialogue.

International Obesity Task Force (IOTF)
www.iotf.org
Click on the About Obesity link for a wide range of useful information.

Internet Fitness Resource (IFR)
www.netsweat.com
The primary purpose of this site is the dissemination of information on exercise and nutrition. IFR offers a comprehensive listing of fitness related sites as well as the Fitness Instructor FAQ, the Fitness Plan, guest editorials, fitness classifieds and more.

Kick!
www.kicksports.com
Kick! is the complete on-line resource for runners, a one-stop reference guide on all aspects of training, racing, nutrition and running gear.

Obesity.com
www.obesity.com
Obesity.com is dedicated to providing practical, up-to-the-minute information about weight loss and obesity. The site provides practical information that supports healthy and practical weight management and weight loss.

Self Improvement Online
www.selfgrowth.com/exercise
Self Improvement Online's site has recommended and reviewed exercise and physical fitness related web sites.

worldfitness.org
www.worldfitness.org
This site aims to inform you of the various aspects of exercise and fitness that can help you enjoy an active life and stay in shape. As well as some useful exercise, fitness and health routines they also offer you the chance to browse through their on-line shopping store, an easy to use storefront giving you access to the latest sporting, exercise and leisure equipment on the Internet.

ADDITIONAL RESOURCES

You might like to contact the following organisations for further information. Due to the increasing cost of postage, many organisations cannot respond to enquiries unless they receive a stamped, addressed envelope.

British Nutrition Foundation (BNF)
High Holborn House
52-54 High Holborn
London
WC1V 6RQ
Tel: 0171 404 6504
Fax: 0171 404 6747
E-mail: british/
nutrition@compuserve.com.
Web site: www.nutrition.org.uk
The BNF is an independent charity which provides reliable information and advice on nutrition and related health matters. They produce a wide range of leaflets, briefing papers and books. Ask for their publications list.

European Food Information Council (EUFIC)
1 Place des Pyramides 75001
Paris
France
Tel: 00 33 140 20 44 40

Fax: 00 33 140 20 44 41
E-mail: eufic@eufic.org
Web site: www.eufic.org
EUFIC is a non-profit-making organisation based in Paris. It has been established to provide science-based information on foods and food-related topics, i.e. nutrition and health, food safety and quality and biotechnology in food for the attention of European consumers. It publishes regular newsletters, leaflets, reviews, case studies and other background information on food issues.

Health Education Authority (HEA)
Trevelyan House
30 Great Peter Street
London
SW1P 2HW
Tel: 0171 222 5300
Fax: 0171 413 8900
Web site: www.hea.org.uk

International Obesity Task Force (IOTF)
231 North Gower Street
London, NW1 2NS
Tel: 0171 691 1900
Fax: 0171 387 6033
E-mail: obesity@iotf.org
Web site: www.iotf.org
The IOTF is working to alert the world to the growing health crisis threatened by soaring levels of obesity.

The Food Commission
94 White Lion Street
London, N1 9PF
Tel: 0171 837 2250
Fax: 0171 837 1141
Web site: www.foodcomm.org.uk
The Food Commission is committed to ensuring good quality food for all. They are a national non-profit organisation campaigning for the right to safe, wholesome food. Publishes *Food Magazine* and other publications.

INDEX

ACKNOWLEDGEMENTS

The publisher is grateful for permission to reproduce the following material.

While every care has been taken to trace and acknowledge copyright, the publisher tenders its apology for any accidental infringement or where copyright has proved untraceable. The publisher would be pleased to come to a suitable arrangement in any such case with the rightful owner.

Chapter One: A Question of Fitness

Survival of the fattest, © Emma Haughton, *English are among fattest in Europe*, © The Independent, June 1999, *Fat is a European issue*, © International Obesity Task Force, *Physical activity, body-weight and health*, © European Food Information Council (EUFIC), May 1999, *Nutrition facts on adolescence*, © British Nutrition Foundation (BNF), *No-gym generation*, © The Daily Mail, March 1999, *The joy of exercise*, © The Guardian, May 1999, *Telly turns children into tubbies*, © Telegraph Group Limited, London 1999, *Nutrition facts on obesity*, © British Nutrition Foundation (BNF), *Fast food facts*, © Health Education Authority (HEA), *Junk food is 'health risk to British children'*, © Telegraph Group Limited, London 1999, *Army caves in to the fast food invasion*, © The Daily Mail, January 1999, *Children's diet*, © LACA, April 1999, *Additional findings*, © LACA, *Why being overweight can pile on the years*, © The Daily Mail, August 1999, *Body mass*, © Crown copyright material is reproduced with the permission of the Controller of Her Majesty's Stationery Office, *Can you be fit and fat?*, © The Guardian, July 1999, *Nowadays the fats really do add up*, © The Independent, May 1999, *10 key facts on obesity*, © British Nutrition Foundation (BNF).

Chapter Two: Getting in Shape

The ABCs of exercise, © BUPA/Mosby International, *General exercises*, © Exercise and Fitness on the Web (www.exercise.co.uk), *Exercise for teenagers*, © 1998-1999 drkoop.com, Inc., *Do I really need to warm up?*, © Fitness Management Magazine, Los Angeles, Calif, *Are your trainers fit to take the pace?*, © Telegraph Group Limited, London 1999, *Achieving a balanced diet*, © British Nutrition Foundation (BNF), *Diet and weight*, © BUPA/Mosby International, *Healthy eating – facts and figures*, © Crown copyright material is reproduced with the permission of the Controller of Her Majesty's Stationery Office, *Obesity versus overweight*, © 1997-1999, Intelligent Nutrition Systems, Inc., *Aerobic exercise*, © Exercise and Fitness on the Web (www.exercise.co.uk), *Does exercise affect our mood?*, © 1998-1999 drkoop.com, Inc., *What is cross-training, and why should I do it?*, © 1999 World Fitness, *Exercise and the heart*, © Exercise and Fitness on the Web (www.exercise.co.uk), *Fun and fitness*, © Fun & Fitness, *Pain-free bike riding*, © 1999 Women.com Networks, Inc.

Photographs and illustrations:

Pages 1, 6, 10, 13, 21, 24, 31, 33, 35, 36, 40: Simon Kneebone, pages 5, 8, 18, 25, 29, 32, 34: Pumpkin House.

Craig Donnellan
Cambridge
January, 2000